Dazed and Fatigued

Dazed and Fatigued

*i*n the Toxic 21st Century

*M*ark Llewellyn Hall

CONSAFOS PRESS

Consafos Press
7353 Fountain Avenue
Los Angeles, CA 90046
www.consafos.com

Copyright © 1998, by Mark Llewellyn Hall

Library of Congress Cataloging-In-Publication Data
Hall, Mark Llewellyn, 1968-
    Dazed and fatigued in the toxic 21st century/Mark Llewellyn Hall
    p.   cm.
    ISBN 0-9656535-2-8
    1. Hall, Mark Llewellyn, 1968- —Health. 2. Chronic fatigue
syndrome—Patients—California—Biography.   I. Title.
RB150.F37H36   1998
362.1'960478'0092—dc21
[B]   98-25140
                               CIP

Printed in the United States of America
2 4 6 8 10 9 7 5 3 1

*T*o My Family

Acknowledgments

I would like to express my deepest thanks to the friends, family, advisors, and teachers who supported me on my journey to recovery. Special thanks to my parents, my amazing girlfriend Marisol, my nanna, my grandma, Brenda, and my stepbrother Sean.

I would also like to thank friends Jay Solomon, Chris Williams, Matt Fife, Dave Payne, Siubhan and Mark Lamas, Jana Singer, Alexandra Tremblay, Nick Fowler, and Tina Deranja for their support and insights; Alex Olmedo, Cameron Graham, and Ben Karney for inspirations I will always value.

Finally, I want to thank Daniel Light the greatest herbalist, and his wife Ursula; Craig Marshall with Consafos Press for his guidance; and my editor Deedle Rodriguez.

the candle's always burning, focus on the flame
as you search the backstreets of the world
for god and some kind of reason
                              why you are here

where bead-bearing gurus peddle paradigms
in wood-paneled rooms
but the noise you hear, day in day out,
gets louder, until you're screaming at yourself

so you focus on the flame, but the candle's always burning
and you want to run away to an island paradise—
palm trees and pristine beaches
your hammock hanging right next to your thatch hut
waves gently rolling up the sand

until you discover that the island is inside you
the journey all around you, day in day out
still you're hog-tied to the back of some
crystal-guided hippie bus, traveling cross-country
because Fiji costs too much

all this time the candle's burning,
but now it's burning at both ends
you're feeling frantic, because you're juggling
juggling lives, juggling lies,
juggling family, work, and friends
but you've got too many plates in the air
flying all around you, day in day out
you're feeling really frantic

and when it all comes crashing down
(because it always does)
you feel a shock — the pain of loss and failure
but later you start feeling so much better
the pressure is off and you realize
the candle's always burning
and now you've got time to focus on the flame

*P*art 1:

*T*he Fall

Chapter 1

It hit me like a two-by-four right smack in the face. I woke up dazed, disoriented, my head throbbed, my body ached. The room was spinning. It wasn't a hangover — I had had a few of those. And it wasn't just a cold — I had had a few of those too. When I tried to stand I had to sit back down. My legs buckled beneath me. I laid back on my rumpled bed staring at the ceiling. I could feel my fingers tingling at the tips. There was no question about it. I wasn't just sick — I was SSSIIIIICKKKK!!!!

My muscles felt a little sore the previous day. Nothing out of the unusual given the amount of training I was doing. The Cal Berkeley rugby team would tour the East Coast in late October and this was my senior year — my big year. I lifted religiously all summer and for the first part of the semester. I always had an athletic build, but now I was actually built. I had been running, too. I felt fast. I felt strong. I felt ready.

I had walked back to my apartment after a long hard practice of drills and scrums, dragging my feet like the Hunchback or a Jekyll turned Hyde. My roommate wasn't home. He was supposed to meet some friends of ours to sell them a couple of the raffle tickets I was peddling to pay for my trip to the East Coast. He wasn't going to make it. Sure, I was a little peeved, but sometimes other commitments get in the way get in the way get in the way. Just like sometimes you wish you had done things a little differently than you did. Lying there that morning,

3

I wished I hadn't gone down to meet our friends the previous night.

I was tired but not exhausted, told them I wasn't drinking, gave in to a beer, gave in to one more, an hour into the evening I was tongue-deep in a game of quarters seven pitchers long. We were at Kip's Pizzeria, a second-story pie parlor a few doors down from Telegraph Avenue. My roommate was a pole-vaulter on the track team and the guys I was out with were his teammates, talking all kinds of track. I was peddling my raffle tickets, having a good time.

I always had a good time when I was out with Billy. Billy was the kind of guy you could count on at 2:00 a.m. to open the door to his apartment even though he'd been asleep for over an hour and knew the only reason you'd showed up was to barf in his toilet. He was the kind of guy you'd take on a Dionysian deluge, because he'd party 'til he dropped, taunt you and never stop challenging you to dance naked with a three-legged swine, and while you're smokin' hooch, drinkin' wine, stompin' mud under your bloody feet, he'd be saying, "Okay, now I'll bet you can't ..."

I was no lech. I was no drunk. But I knew how to have a good time. Billy was a damn good friend and we were having one that night. When I walked back up the hill about eleven, I was tired. My friends were just getting started, yet I knew I needed sleep. Let myself into my place, brushed my teeth, took off my clothes, and climbed into bed for a night of hard-earned rest.

It hit me like a two-by-four right smack in the face. My night of hard-earned rest became a day of laboriously endured fatigue, which then became two, then three, then four, laid up and crashed out. I started drinking a lot of water, gallon by gallon, I drank and I drank — vitamin C tea with orange juice and soup. But, I wasn't getting better. Knew something was seriously wrong when my entire body went numb with needles and I was forced to trudge to Cowell Hospital less than a quarter mile from my apartment and I didn't know if I would make it. Didn't know if my body could take it, could take the trip, because my mind was trippin', a fiery blur. My thoughts fuzzy and then forgotten.

"Ahh, it's probably just the flu."

"But my body's numb."

"Take Tylenol for your headache, get lots of rest, it will probably be gone in a couple of weeks."

"It's been a couple weeks. I'm leaving for the East Coast Friday."

"We've checked you for Mononucleosis, Epstein Barr virus, Cytomeglovirus, Lyme Disease, HIV, and Worms. Your tests have revealed nothing. Try doing a little exercise, stimulate the immune system. You'll get better, nothing to worry about — come back in a week. You'll see, just a bad flu going around this year, didn't have your flu shot this year did you, no I didn't think so, go home get some rest, everything's going to be fine, it just takes time that's all."

Who's got time, time to watch the world go by, time to let those you once led march right past you, right over you, right through you? They look back over their shoulders and claim they've seen you lying there the whole time, just another lazy sloth. When you gonna get up, man!

I went to the East Coast despite the fact I was so tired I slept in the airport, slept on the plane, and slept when I arrived at Dartmouth the first stop on our East Coast tour. The leaves were changing — orange, yellow, red, brown, before they fell to the ground. We drove in vans, sleeping on couches cold from the lack of heat in the fraternity houses in which we were being housed.

That's the way it is on tour. The accommodations are never great, you rarely get a bed, but the guys from the other teams go out of their way to show you a good time. You get a decent meal after the games — pasta served from buckets, salad served from coolers, plump pink dogs and thick juicy burgers with all the trimmings, and kegs of cold beer, usually Budweiser or Coors. Sometimes girls show up at the parties. Usually they don't. Rugby players can be obnoxious, downright delinquent. Some code written by some toad long ago says: act like an idiot, treat women like shit, it's cool to be a fool, just watch where I spit.

I'm not saying it's right or even that it's always so, and most of the guys are good intelligent individuals. But, put a group of rugby players in a room, close the door, and it becomes a game of who can out defile the foulest foe, score the biggest ho, and tell the tallest tale toe to toe — all these sparring egos, sparring for the spotlight.

I would have been right there with them, for I generally tried to lead the pack. But I was sick, a sour face. I slept a lot, didn't play. Thought I would get better as the trip went on, and I did. Even thought about playing in our final match against Boston College, but decided I was kidding myself. My coach didn't want me to suffer a setback, so I sat back and watched; watched as everyone else played, watched as everyone else had a good time, pretending I was having one too.

I arrived back in Berkeley a week later, another week behind in my work. I felt better, but I just didn't feel the same. I didn't feel sound, as if there were holes in my pockets where the change was sneaking through.

I remember calling one of the girls I had been dating. Jennifer graduated a couple years before, but we still saw each other off and on. It was something we were used to, a habit we didn't quite know how to quit. On the phone I was frustrated, crying. I started to let my fears be known, when she scolded me like a ten year old. Told me to stop crying. Told me there were people who were paralyzed from the waist down. People starving in Guyana. People with holes in their head so big you could see clear through to the other side. Said I had nothing to cry about. "It's just the flu." Said when the doctors told her she had mono, she drank water all day and cured herself. Said with people suffering the way they do, who was I to cry about the flu. What about them? What about the hungry, the tired, the tempest-tossed yearning to be free?

What about them I thought as I hung up the phone. Can't even call someone I care about, someone I thought cared for me, to get a little support. I wonder if the tempest-tossed-yearning showed up at her door, would she help them? Or would she scream at them to stop their complaining, too?

I broke up with her during Thanksgiving vacation, or she broke up with me. Said she wanted to be friends. Felt I was too needy. Felt we'd gone on far too long. What could I say — she was right. But why is it when you're down that's when you get dumped, drop-kicked, paddled with a stick. It happens sometimes — happens all the time — until you realize you're hanging around the wrong people.

I was angry. I was alone. Drifted so far from my family, I couldn't really talk to them. Actually, drifted isn't quite the word — broke away, severed, split. I was an only child whose parents worked long hours, late into the night, on the fast track to success. So many nights coming home to an empty house to face the hollow, to face the cold, to face the darkness, to face the fact I was all alone. I spent my time with friends. The older I got, the more time with friends I spent. It's not that my parents didn't care. It's not that they weren't there when I really needed them. I just hated to be alone. Hated having to depend on my parents, my family split from a long-drawn divorce too confusing to understand. When I went to college, I had no plans of coming back. I was forging my own life. Spent a summer in Europe, spent a summer in D.C. I didn't want to depend on anyone ever again. Didn't want to give them the chance to let me down, let me down, let me drown. It had been so long since I depended on anyone for support, I forgot how. I didn't know how to reach out. I was angry. I was alone.

When you're young, healthy, illness isn't something you understand. You get a cold, you get better. Feel a little tired, you go anyway. You've got so much going on, you don't have time to be sick, time to be tired, time to be laid up, down and out, drowning in your fears. So the world went on around me — students partied, athletes competed, classes continued, and I did too.

I started working out again, started going out again. I had a few beers here and there, ran a few laps here and there. But things weren't the same. I wasn't myself. I got tired just as I got going. Days seemed to drag, like I was dragging the day slowly behind me on a long noose.

I love you on a stick. I love you on a stake. Luv you on a stick. Luv you on a stake. Stake. Stake. What a mistake. Hate. What a mistake. So much hate. Hate. Hate. Anyway ... My roommate bought a little Christmas tree, like the one in *Merry Christmas, Charlie Brown*. I hung some ornaments on it, branches so thin, tree so small, it bowed. So small and awkward, yet I loved that little tree. I loved the spirit it inspired. I would stare at it, autumn nights getting cold and dark; tree lights on autumn nights — red, blue, green, magenta, and white, with a little star on top. Something to hold on to. It brought me home, back to my childhood. It recaptured a piece of myself from a time I left behind long ago. Christmas with family. Hot apple cider, gazing into a blazing fire on a cold winter's night. So much love in that little tree, so much love brought back to me.

The semester ended. The season of merry, jolly, and joy arrived, but still no jingle in my bells. I drove home to Los Angeles with a couple friends in the back of a blue Dodge Van, white stripe peeling off its side. Driving down 101 from Berkeley, we got our first view of the Pacific after passing San Luis Obispo, the sun setting, Clapton's *Wonderful Tonight* in stereo sound. We talked about what Christmas vacation held in store for each of us. New Year's Eve. Presents under a decadent tree. Parties with friends. Parties that didn't end. Skiing. Bitty Betty Ski Bunny Babes in skintight pants. We talked politics. Played the roles of protagonist, antagonist, nihilist, and sycophant.

We even started talking about the drive back up, but in the back of my mind, I kept thinking — I did it! I finished out the semester. Still no jingle in my bells, but I was feeling better. I would continue to feel better. Missed my opportunity to play rugby on the East Coast tour, but I'd be back. Not playing would serve to make my return that spring all the sweeter. Three weeks of Christmas vacation was just enough time to get my body well, healthy, revived; to get my body back into the swing ... to get my body back.

I arrived at my doorstep Tuesday night.
"Thanks for the ride. That was a lot of fun."
"Did you get everything?"
"Yeah."
"Call me in a couple weeks if you need a ride back up."
"All right."
"Take it easy. Merry Christmas."
"Yeah. Merry Christmas to you, too."
My mom let me in. Happy to see me. Happy to see her only son, her only child. Wondering how I was feeling. Wondering how the drive went. Wondering how my exams went. Wondering. Wondering. Wondering.

I told her I was feeling pretty good, almost back to normal. Told her the drive went well. Told her my exams went well. Told her it was good to see her. Told her it was good to be home.

I received a couple phone calls. One from a high school friend about a Christmas party the following night out in Brentwood. Another from a fraternity brother about a Christmas party the night after that in Hancock Park.
"Everyone is going to be there."
"Everyone?"
"Everyone."
"Then so am I," thought I.

I went to both parties. Stayed out late the first night. Too late. Two o'clock in the morning. Didn't drink, though. I was excited to see my friends, friends I saw only during Christmas vacation, and summer. Spent the previous summer in Washington D.C. and hadn't seen most of these people in a while — a long while. For some I wish it had been longer, but most I felt glad to see. It was the kind of crowd where you had to say the right things, at the right time, in the right way. You had to look good saying it, at the right time, in the right way. Chest out. Shoulders high. Big smile. Shake hands. Kiss cheeks. Look over here at these tasty treats — Swedish meatballs,

Fettucini Alfredo with chicken and pine nuts, fruit tarts, chocolate darts, Sangria.

The second night I went out, same thing, similar crowd, less food, more alcohol. Coat. Tie. Starched shirt. But this time I started drinking. Had a few beers, a couple of cocktails. I started drinking again the previous month. Not a lot, but it wasn't out of the ordinary either. So I got buzzed, got smoozed, got tired, and drove home.

Woke up groggy tired, rolled out of bed. Feet flat on the cold carpet floor. A bang at the door? No, it's my head. It was the morning of Christmas Eve. A group of us gathered at my old high school for our traditional Christmas Rugby Match. A tradition started my junior year in high school. A tradition that pitted the Old Boys — high school graduates — against the Young Boys — those still in high school. A tradition grown more and more competitive, as the young boys too, became old boys. We played together as teammates in high school, some of us in college. We invited friends of friends to play, players still in high school to play. Parents came to watch. Like a stocking hung from the mantle over a warm wood burning fire, Christmas Rugby had become an integral part of Christmas itself. A time to see old friends, coaches. A time to visit a place, where everybody knows your name and they're always glad you came. All this as part of the game.

Didn't play that day. Took a short run that morning, but something wasn't right. Logs in my Levi's. Had to watch from the sidelines, the saddle-lines, 'cause I was saddled with rage, saddled with fear. Something wasn't right. Game comes once each year, then it's gone. I wanted to play. By not playing I was admitting to myself I couldn't play, admitting I didn't feel good enough to play; admitting — something wasn't right.

Dinner that night. Christmas Eve dinner at the house of my best friend from high school. Part of the tradition, because we're lost without tradition. But, dinner seemed long, seemed to drag on. "Twenty more minutes," I announced. Though I was tired, I was still having fun. Then, twenty minutes later, "twenty minutes more.

10

The Fall

Dessert, then I'm out the door." Twenty minutes later, wasn't feeling right, but "twenty minutes more."

Nothing conscious about it. I didn't know it, but some part of me could sense I was holding onto something that would soon be stolen from me. Squeezed like blood from my veins. Was it my freedom? My friends? My structure? My dreams? I didn't know exactly what I stood to lose. All I knew was that I was holding onto it that night, cradling it the way a boy cradles his bear before the onset of a terrible storm. I talked to everyone once, twice. Said my goodbyes. Said everything was real nice.

It hit me like a two-by-four right smack in the face. Blood on my hands. Bloody my space. I relapsed on Christmas morning. Made it down to open my presents. Rip. Tear. Torn. Wrapping strewn across the living room floor. Tinsel and trinkets. Shirts and pants. Watched the Sugar Plum Fairies dance. Chocolates. Egg Nog. Plastic wood burning log. Pictures with me holding up this. Pictures of me holding up that. Soon we were done. Man, that was fun!

I walked upstairs and spent the rest of the day in bed. And the next day. And the next. And then everyone went back to school, but me. I stayed home. Confused. Tired. Frightened. I was all alone.

*C*hapter 2

Growing up, I drove my fancy car to my fancy high
school, comfort and structure with so many rules. Handed
me my life, like a roasted hen on a silver platter, and
I swallowed it like a good little boy. Well ... maybe not
that good, but I swallowed it just the same. Guess I liked
the way people smiled at me as I chewed the fat. Liked the
taste of golden chicken in my mouth.

But even in my earliest memories, I recall feeling some
part of my life incomplete, missing. I yearned for
something more — more love, more peace, more action,
more release. Never could quite put my finger on what
that *more* might be. How could I obtain it? I had
imagined myself running away to a tropical island in the
South Pacific. Like Gauguin, I'd live in a thatch hut,
commune with the natives. Palm trees. Pristine beaches.
I would find myself — my essence — in the solitude
overlooking a wide Sargasso Sea.

How ironic that through illness, in the confines of my
quiet room, my fantasy in some strange, cruel way was
finally fulfilled. My bed, a solitary island. My sea, the
green expanse of carpet that stretched the floor between
where I laid sick, rolled up in blankets, and the cabinet that
housed our twenty-inch Sony television set. My trees, the
Ficus and the Delphinium which kept me company as the
days dragged doggedly on. Yet, this was no warm windless tropical island, days spent reviving my soul, frolicking
in the surf, picking coconuts from trees, building castles in

the sand. This was cold, lonely, tired. This was wilderness, laid up in dark winter.

I spent three months watching television — a TV flunky, surfing the shows and spanking the monkey. Like a bad cold, figured I could cure my malaise through some serious R&R, but I was wrong. The more I laid around, the worse I felt.

I visited doctors who gave fancy names to my illness: Chronic Fatigue Syndrome; Chronic Fatigue Immune Deficiency; Post Viral Neurasthenia; Post Viral Fatigue Syndrome. They gave fancy explanations as to why I felt so dead, like lead. Each explanation cost me a little more money, a little more patience, a lot more frustration, because nothing worked. I tried numerous and various treatments. With each new treatment tried and failed, the truth became a little clearer — despite their explanations, science did not know why I felt the way I did.

Try some of this. Try some of that. Vitamins A, B, C, D, and E. Herbs. Herbal remedies. Homeopathic Remedies. Vitamin shots. Shots of Gamma Globulin. Spoonfuls and thimblefuls. Drops and teas. Concoctions that gave me hives. Concoctions that made me sneeze. Go ask Alice when she's ten feet tall — one pill makes you smaller, the other makes you tall. Lost thirty pounds in three months — almost one-fifth my body's natural weight. Lost confidence in my doctors. Lost confidence in myself. Until I threw every last treatment, every last potion, every bottle and all its poison down the drizzling drain. Walked out into the windy rain and screamed, "I've had enough!"

What do you do when you realize you have no real control over your life? Where do you go? Go to school, get smart, get fit, get organized. You set goals, achieve goals. You have an idea of what you want to be, where you want to go, who you want to go there with. But you can't control the onset of a serious illness. Can't control the world around you. Can't stop the slip-slide of an oncoming truck, the riptide that sucks you up. Take precautions. Take care of yourself. But, where do you

turn when your life takes a turn? Where do you turn,
cause life turns like a snake in and out of holes, slithering
along — sometimes slower than fast, sometimes faster
than slow.

Al was a real estate agent, working for my mom.
Couldn't quite figure out how to market the house.
The style of the house was modern industrial. My dad
designed and built it ten years before. He called it
"The Silo House." It had Corrugated Asbestos siding with
glass sliding doors outside. Wood beam ceilings with
exposed plastic and copper plumbing inside. One week Al
called it form following function; the next, function
following form. Sometimes he presented it as a work of
art; sometimes as a work of artifice. Suffice it to say, Al
never sold our house.

He brought me a book each week he came, and when
he came, we talked about my illness and ways to get better.
We talked about *The Way of the Peaceful Warrior*. We
talked about the role of *Serendipity*. We talked about staying *Fit for Life*.

With the knowledge I gained from the books, from our
talks, and other sources of information, I started to put
together a healing program. I began by changing my diet.
Started eating more fruits and vegetables, less meat and
dairy. Tried food-combining, eating proteins — tofu, fish,
nuts, beans — and starches — pasta, rice, bread — at
separate meals. Tried macrobiotics, cooking and heating
everything I ate. Tried raw foods consumption, eating
everything I ate raw and uncooked. Never held onto any
one belief too long. I assembled pieces of this, pieces of
that. Tried natural food supplements. Supplements that
didn't upset my stomach. Wheat grass drinks. Carrot
juice. All the time eliminating more and more processed
foods, animal products — meat, fish, dairy — and buying
more and more organically-grown grains and vegetables.

I no longer merely fueled my body, feeding my hunger.
Consumption became part of a larger process. The kitchen
became my playground — chopping, slicing, mixing,
folding. I fried, filleted, baked, and broiled. Colorful
sights, heavenly scents, flavors to tease, treat, and tantalize

my taste buds. I cooked Szechwan stir-fries, coconut curries, cornbread with rosemary, black bean chili, and mango chutney on short grain brown rice. I prepared salads and sauces, sauces for my salads. I experimented with culinary styles from Hong Kong to Jamaica, Tuscany to Thailand. Too tired to visit the world, so I brought the world home to visit me.

When I started feeling better, Al took me to my first Hatha Yoga class. We had talked about it for several weeks. Discussed the benefits of a strong, limber body, and a peaceful mind.

The class was held at a non-profit AIDS support center in Hollywood. The place was clean, neat, comfortable. A large family-style porch led into a whitewashed interior with artwork on the walls, painted by center staff members and patients. As I walked in, I took a moment to sift through the pamphlets, ad-hoc of literature, and leaflets stacked neatly on a large oak table near the entrance. Healing seminars. Support counseling. Massage. This wasn't just an old twenties style home converted into an AIDS center, it was an AIDS center that functioned as a home.

The instructor donated her time to teach the class. Many of the people taking her class were HIV positive or worked in conjunction with the center. All the men taking the class were gay. Al was gay. And given that I arrived with Al, everyone taking the class including our instructor assumed I was gay, too. They assumed we were a couple. Instead of being addressed separately, individually, we were a unit:

"How are you doing back there, Mark *and* Al."

"Everything alright, Mark *and* Al?"

"Mark *and* Al, make sure you get a good stretch on this one. That's it Mark *and* Al. Little bit lower Mark *and* Al. Great, now breathe, Mark *and* Al."

Made me feel a little uncomfortable at first. If I were someone less secure with my masculinity, I would have run high-hither for the door, as they smothered me with innuendoes, references, nods, and winks. I guess in a community persecuted by ignorance, intolerance, negligence and fear, the only remedy to persecution is a strong acceptance. Your relationship isn't just acknowledged — it's hailed! I felt like saying, "Look, you've got me pegged all wrong. I'm not gay. We're not together. We're not really even friends. Al is my mom's real estate agent."

But I chose not to make an issue out of it. I knew I wasn't gay. If I stuck around long enough, everyone in class would know it, too. So, I just smiled a wide smile, grinned like a wise old dog that remembers every beef bone he's buried under a patchwork pile of grass and sod the size of the Super Bowl, and continued stretching, posing — inhale, exhale ... release.

I started going every Friday, each week learning a little more about my body. I learned about my chakras — my seven energy centers. That these chakras could be awakened through breathing exercises, stretches and postures. That when awakened, my body would heal faster, my mind would become more peaceful, my spirit more fulfilled.

During class, to facilitate the healing process, our instructor guided us through a chakra meditation that progressed up the body, each chakra representing a different level of physical, emotional, and spiritual awareness. Chakras one, two, and three, located at the base of the spine, the genitals, and the navel are the carnal centers that hunger for food, sex, and power.

"Visualize light, spinning over your lower chakras. Over each chakra, visualize a different color. Red. Orange. Yellow. Feel them open. Feel the energy coursing through your body."

"Visualize your heart chakra — the center of centers. The place where all life begins. Where love, compassion, and a sense of community reside. See the light healing you, restoring your body." And finally, she took us through chakras five, six, and seven, located at the larynx, the place just between your eyes, and the crown of your head. These are the spiritual centers connecting us to God, universe, and to infinity, where we realize we are more than our experiences. Our lives just a small blip in time, because we are time, we are forever, beyond ego, everything and nothing all at once. Break on through to the seventh chakra and life as an individual ceases to exist, because in that instant we become life itself.

Didn't achieve nirvana in my first month. Didn't achieve it in my second, or my third, fourth, fifth. But I was going to. If I couldn't be back at school partying with my friends, downing beers carelessly. If I couldn't be playing rugby with my teammates, and finishing my degree. If I couldn't be doing what I wanted to be doing. If I had to suffer through an illness that refused to go away, to let me play (or was it I who refused to let myself play), then Godfuckingdammit I was going to achieve enlightenment.

I would be perfect, shed all my faults and fears. I would be like Mohammed. The Buddha. Christ. My life would mark the second coming — the dawn of a new era. This was merely a test of my strength and worth. Like Edgar in Shakespeare's *King Lear*, I had fallen from grace, fallen flat on my face, cast from the garden that was my life, into wilderness. But I would pull through. I would be healthy again. Mark Hall, a man barely alive. I could rebuild. When I did, I would be better than I was before — better, stronger, faster, wiser ... you get the trip.

Started meditating three times a day — morning, noon, and night. Sitting cross-legged in the quiet corner of my room, I would let my mind go silent, each thought patiently put to rest. Every tension dissolved, until I was free from my day-to-day struggle, free from the illness that would not go away. I could feel the cold flow of air entering my nostrils, and the warm air dispelled. I could hear the silence around me coming to life, the wind rustling through the trees, the birds chirping, and then the hum of silence itself. Colors painted in mushroom clouds on the canvass of my mind, sitting in my space, but moving through another place — Aladdin on a magic carpet ride, surfing the ethereal tide.

This was just part of my regimen. I say regimen, because that's what it was. Something to give me structure, where I had none. I needed sign-posts, field markers, something to strive for. I lived most of my life as an over-achiever, setting goals, setting standards. Now my goal was to get better. So, I measured my life in minutes: wake up at 9:00 a.m., drink my Green Magma, drink my orange juice; take my shower at 9:15; stretch and meditate until 10:00; breakfast at 10:15; take my walk at 10:30.

Measured my life in feet — walk through the neighborhood, a little farther each day, a little harder each day. Tomorrow I will walk to the sign. Tomorrow I will walk to the end of the block, to the end of the street, to the foot of the hill, to the top of the hill. Day after day. Week after week. Sometimes in my frustration, in my desire to be better, I pushed myself too hard, walked myself too far and had to start all over again. Day after day, week after week.

Measured my day by the pages of the books I read — fifty pages a day. Books became my passion. I began with thrillers by authors like Stephen King, Robert Ludlum and Tom Clancy. Sat biting my nails, riding steel rails through Europe and the Middle East. The more I read, the more I wanted to read. I moved into the classics, reading Dosteyevsky's *Crime and Punishment*, F. Scott Fitzgerald's *Tender is the Night*, and Thomas Mann's *The Magic Mountain*.

Reading *The Magic Mountain*, I discovered my favorite character in all of literature — Mynheer Peeperkorn. Mynheer Peeperkorn is an absurd character in many ways. An old colonial Dutch coffee planter who speaks incoherently, Peeperkorn communicates through gestures. Through the passion behind his obscure utterances. And for his passion he is viewed as eloquent. A man of conviction. He explains that:

> Feeling ... is the masculine force that rouses life. Life slumbers. It needs to be roused, to be awakened to a drunken marriage with divine feeling. For feeling ... is godlike. Man is godlike, in that he feels. He is the feeling of God. God created him in order to feel through him ... If man fails in feeling it is blasphemy; it is the surrender of His masculinity, a cosmic catastrophe, an irreconcilable horror ...

18

The Fall

Can't say I support all Mann's beliefs with regard to God and His masculinity, but to the essence of his words, I could relate. As a young man I was cut off from feeling. So many people telling me not to cry, not to love. Be a man. Be strong. Be hard. And here this absurd old man tells me my failure to feel is worse than wrong — it's blasphemy, cosmic catastrophe. When I read it, a small part of me gave way. A door opened. But what did he mean, rouse life through feeling?

Then I read Gabriel Garcia-Marquez, *Love in the Time of Cholera.* The story of a man who falls in love with a woman. Spends his entire life with the hope she might return his love. When he is eighty years old, the woman's husband dead, he starts to write her letters to support her in the loss of her husband. They become friends, and finally at the very end of his long life, lovers. It's not just the story, anyone can write passionately about love. Garcia-Marquez writes passionately about everything. The streets. The gutters in the town in which the man lives. The rivers on which the man's shipping empire is built. The rivers down which the bodies of men and women dead from cholera float. Every time I picked up the book, I felt it come alive in my hands, and knew that to hold life with reverence, the beauty and the horror, was the only way to live my life — to rouse life with feeling.

What floats like a feather and stings like a wasp? By early summer I was much improved, the stark cold days of winter behind me. I got out a couple times each day. I enjoyed eating breakfast, lunch, and dinner on our patio overlooking the hills of Griffith Park — the beige sprawl of Glendale and Burbank in the distance. I enjoyed the peaceful afternoons, a warm summer breeze blowing through my home, reading my books and sipping tea at sunset. I had learned to live with my illness and adapted my purpose to the pursuit of health. I wasn't exactly happy about it, but I was dealing with it.

I lost contact with many of my friends. Most were still back at school and couldn't understand why I wasn't better. Some felt frustrated because I was taking things slowly and thought I wasn't doing enough to improve. Others felt I had "given in" to my illness.

"You know, you've got to get out more, take a job, take a trip, go to the beach. Tell yourself you're just gonna do it. You can't just lie there and do nothing — you'll never get better."

Truth was, I wanted to get out. But it seemed like every time I tried to do something beyond my every day routine, I felt worse. Seemed like I was standing in a garden of opportunity, but every time I reached out to touch the flowers, someone/something out there/somewhere smack-swack-cracked my hand and sent me back to my place, sitting me back down. So I stayed home where I felt safe, and stuck to my routine.

At the same time, I didn't want to get out, clinging to my vanity, holding onto the facade. I lost a lot of weight. Didn't look like my old athletic self. I had grown accustomed to being in the thick of the action, the man on the move, pitching stories of glory to the rest of the room. Now I had no stories to tell and felt like no one wanted to hear about my illness — too close to home. I felt like no one wanted to hear about the books I read, my changing diet, my changing ideas. Too much going on, too little going wrong in their lives to listen to the misery/mystery in mine. I just didn't feel people would accept me the way I was. Felt I had little to offer, a magician whose magic was gone. So I stayed home where I felt safe, and stuck to my routine.

I was facing other problems as well. Sleepless nights, awake until dawn. I remember not going to sleep until the paper boy/man drove by to deliver the paper at 6:00 a.m. Every time he did, I thought of ways to sabotage his little truck — pop a tire, rig a wire to a bomb and blow that son-of-a-bitch sky-high. The paper boy/man had become a symbol of my sleepless nights. The whine of his engine, an emblem of my enduring fatigue.

"Not again," I would grumble, as I tossed about my pillow too large, too soft, so terribly, damnably, miserably uncomfortable. Then I'd think, "How can I get better, if I can't get any sleep?" as I'm shifting, contorting from side-to-side. Legs. Arms. Head. Hair, tangled in this tiresome, all-too-familiar unrest.

My obsessive pursuit to achieve enlightenment, like some trophy to be won, like some degree of merit to be earned, caused me further problems. Visiting my father at his home in Toronto, I picked up a book entitled *Hatha Yoga*. The book illustrated many of the basic yoga postures and talked about *prana* (meaning "breath" or "breathing") as an important aspect of the life force/life energy that heals each one of us and keeps us vital. It discussed the yogi masters and their ability to control breathing, that the slightest breath sustains them hours at a time. I thought:

"I'm going to be like them — a yogi master. I'll gain control over my breath. Teach myself to restrain my breathing to the point where it seems to others I'm not breathing at all. I'll gain mastery over my body and its healing functions, so that eventually my body will no longer hold mastery over me."

Despite the warnings not to attempt breath restraint without the tutelage of a trained master, I forged ahead. I practiced every day, first for twenty minutes, then thirty, then forty-five, an hour. I breathed slower and slower, my breath a faint whisper, and envisioned the dead calm on a windless ocean.

I spent so much time controlling my breathing, I forgot how to breathe normally. Got to the point where I could barely breathe at all. Felt like I was suffocating, like I couldn't get any air into my throat, because my throat closed down — a sock in my esophagus. The irony! The lunacy! I was trying too hard to get better. Forcing myself, like Pooh stuck in Rabbit's house, tasting too much tainted honey, too many magic beans. I was stuck, getting more stuck, and couldn't get free.

When struggling through periods of turmoil, you're up and down so much you can feel like you're living in a state of perpetual gyration. It's important to have constants. It's important to have a place you can go to escape the turmoil, the tumult that spins you round and round, keeps you hovering ten feet off the ground. It's important to find a way to release your frustration, release your anger, release your rage. If you don't, the anger turns inward. It eats at you. It leads to destructive behavior, lashing out at those you love, lashing out at yourself.

While growing up in high school and college, I was always active in sports. I loved it for the competition, the camaraderie, the release. Took my anger out on the field. I'm not condoning it. I'm not chastising it. The field was the one place where I felt safe letting everything out. Fighting got me detention. Yelling at my parents got me grounded. On the field I could scream, and that was psych. I could pummel my opponent, and that was intensity. I could run till I dropped; run till every last drop of rage, like sweat, poured through my skin, and that was hustle.

When I got sick, letting my anger and frustration out on the field was no longer an option. I couldn't play sports. I didn't have the energy. Every time I tried to walk or jog off anger, I felt worse. I risked relapse.

While talking to an old girlfriend on the phone, I mentioned I wanted to learn to play guitar. Told her my days seemed long, that I longed for something to do, some way to fill my time otherwise spent reading, or watching television.

"I've got a guitar," she said.

"Do you play?"

"No. I wanted to learn, but didn't have the patience. In fact, now it's just sitting in my closet, collecting dust. Would you like to borrow it?"

"Are you serious?"

"I'm completely serious."

She brought it over the next day. The guitar case was dusty, old and broken down, but the guitar itself was in excellent condition. I started by learning how to tune it. The strings were old and lifeless, but I couldn't tell that at the time. Didn't even consider having it restrung, because I didn't realize it needed it. I was just happy learning to play.

She brought song books with her, too. Once I figured out how to tune the guitar, I learned a few basic chords with the help of *Mel Bay's Guitar Chords in Picture and Diagram Form.* I started playing songs from the *Peaceful Easy Feelings Volume II* songbook for easy guitar. Songs from the 70s. Songs I remembered listening to as a kid.

No one ever showed me how to strum the guitar. For the first few months I strummed in one direction — down. You can imagine the revelation I experienced, when I walked into a music shop to purchase a new song book and a man played one of the songs from a book I considered buying.

"You mean you can strum up, too?"

"Yeah, of course," he said with an incredulous look on his face.

"No ... uh ... I mean ... uh ... what's that rhythm you were just playing?"

"Oh here, let me show you."

"Hey, that's pretty cool. Thanks."

"Anytime."

I played the guitar daily, getting better and better. Practicing fulfilled my need for accomplishment and became my primary means of release.

sometimes when I don't have time to cry
I reach for my guitar—
the company of a cherished friend.
tuned just right, its mahogany body sings to me
rocking me back and forth
working my way up the neck
it's the wine of the strings that soothes me.

when I can't bear to feel
I grab my guitar—
the buoy that rescues a drowning man.
I pick out a base line deep and rhythmic
or a melody smooth and sweet.

like two streams that merge
I become one with the guitar,
and together we weep
fingers flying over strings,
together we feel
my spirit soaring with them.

I started seeing a therapist. I needed the view of an onlooker, an unbiased third party. My family was fairly supportive, encouraging, but many times I found them more upset than I about my illness. When I went to them feeling down, and tried to express my fears, my grief, my uncertainty, they were never addressed.

Instead of hearing: "It's going to be okay. You're doing fine. It's just going to take time. Be patient. You'll get better."

I frequently heard: "Oh god, this is terrible. Maybe we should take you to another doctor, an acupuncturist, a chiropractor, get you into aromatherapy. Someone told me about a homeopath in Cleveland who ..."

Every time I brought up the fact I felt terrible, I found myself consoling someone in some way. Found myself trying to defray a Pandora's box of ideas and concerns, not to mention tears. I wasn't open to new ideas, or willing to submit myself to the whims of another half-baked, high-priced crackpot, who through his/her quackery only made me sicker. I was tired of consoling people, when I was the one who felt like death on a day bed warmed over once.

I first went to see Michelle in late April. Her small office, set up in the back house of her home in Pacific Palisades, was comfortable — wicker chairs, lace drapes and a lie-down couch with oversized cushions. Shade trees outside the office made it seem cool and peaceful inside, a retreat from the congestion, the heat that by late spring can be unbearable in Los Angeles.

I liked her immediately. Something about her demeanor that was every bit as comfortable as her office. She just seemed grounded, in touch, evolved. Maybe it was the years she worked as a counselor at the Simonton Cancer Center. Maybe it was the years she spent counseling people living with both long term and life threatening illnesses. Maybe she was just an amazingly kind person.

For one hour each week, she listened to my stories objectively, without passing judgment. She worked with me, helping me to set goals. Not goals that were achievement-oriented, but goals to expand the quality of my life in certain areas: relating to friends and family; spending time in nature; spending time with myself; working towards getting better through acceptance of my illness, instead of seeing it as something I was fighting. A battle. A struggle against a worthy opponent. I started to view it as part of a more complex healing process, which involved not only the body, but the mind and the spirit as well. By healing my mind and my spirit, my body would follow.

When I ran into stumbling blocks — frustrations born from setbacks in my health — she used hypnosis and visualization, taking me to a place within myself where I could feel safe, see myself completely healthy, and watch my body being healed.

As the summer progressed, I grew healthier and healthier. Took longer walks. Spent more time with friends. Spent some time with my father in Toronto. As the new school year approached, I made plans for my return, applied for re-admittance, signed up for classes and secured a place to live.

"I don't know if I'm totally healthy yet," I remember saying on my last visit to see Michelle.

"I don't know if I'm ready to go back to school. Ready to face my friends. Ready to live on my own, now that I have been living at home. Ready to start over. Ready to try again."

"You're ready," she said.

*C*hapter 3

This is the dawning of the age of Asparagus.
Everything green, cropped at the root. Rain forests.
Timberlands. All by the hands of man to feed people.
People popping up like little shoots and spears. Fifty million
in Zaire. Two hundred million in Indonesia. One and a
quarter billion in China by the year 2000. In Berkeley, you
can't help hearing about overpopulation, mass starvation,
ozone holes, animals maimed in the name of research, gay
rights, Right to Life. Chiming, whining, everybody trying
to argue their point, stand their ground — a cause for all
occasions, if you have not a cause found.

Standing at the corner of Bancroft Way and Telegraph
Avenue on any given day, you might be approached by
Hari Krishnas, Black Nationalists, AIDS activists and
someone representing the Democratic National Party
Caucus. In the background, you would hear the music of a
Brazilian Salsa Band, Jamaican Steel Drums, and a man
named Rick Starr, singing songs by Frank Sinatra in a
voice so out of key, your first thought is, "I think my
hearing's gone bad."

If you took a moment to watch the people walk by, you
would note that virtually every social group would be
represented. Every race. Every religion. Most countries.
You might see a professor, fresh from alcohol rehab wearing
a Grateful Dead T-Shirt headed to a rally to fight
homelessness. Or a student — half-Black, half-Asian,
born-again Christian — en route from his/her

fraternity/sorority house to meet his/her Hungarian Molecular Biology Science Lab partner at a restaurant called The Hofbrau House for bratwurst and beer. Or homeless midgets. The Polka Dot man. Stony Burke, Rare, Andre the Giant and the Bubble Lady. A woman taking her pig and her goat for a walk through campus. The paths you take in Berkeley can lead you anywhere, and all paths lead back to Berkeley.

Found my way back on a DC-9. Arrived Saturday morning into Oakland Airport, the sun shining in a cloudless sky overhead. Called Matt, a fraternity brother of mine, who agreed to pick me up and said I could stay at his place until my apartment was ready.

Apartments are like commodities in Berkeley. Once you find a good one, you sign your name to the lease and keep it, pass it down to friends and fraternity members. My apartment had been occupied by members of our fraternity for eight years. During the semester, when I withdrew from school, my name stayed on the lease. In my absence, my former roommate — also a fraternity brother — sub-leased the place to a couple girls for the summer. They were still occupying it. Though I wanted to, I couldn't kick them out for another couple of days.

We stopped on the way back from the airport to have lunch in a small coffee house on College Avenue. A new place I had never been before. I was so excited to be back amongst the living, back amongst my friends. I ordered black bean vegetarian chili, which came with a crusty sourdough roll. Matt and I talked about the coming semester, caught up on who was doing what, living where, and with whom. As I stared out at the different people walking by, I noticed that my food tasted better than it had while down in L.A. The colors seemed brighter, the faces friendlier. As we got up to leave, I tipped the waitress some ridiculous amount, wondering when I became so generous. I was so excited to be back. Felt so good to be back.

I looked a little different than when I left Berkeley eight months before. I was extremely thin. You might even say emaciated. I went from a well-built hundred and sixty pounds, to a very skinny hundred and thirty pounds.

I grew a beard while visiting my father in Canada. Kept it short, well-groomed, but the overall effect was that most people did not recognize me at first sight. Familiar faces passed me on the street, but never stopped to talk, never paused to say hi. I was myself, but I wasn't me. I recognized them, but no one recognized me.

That suited me just fine. Didn't really want to be recognized. I liked the idea of traveling incognito, underground, like the invisible man, or a Connecticut Yankee in King Arthur's court. I was home, but in a different dimension, a different period of time than the one I occupied before. Instead of falling back into the same old scene, I enjoyed the possibility of checking out new scenes, new places where my former self would have felt uncomfortable, out of place. The prospects for new adventures were everywhere, and I entertained them all.

Back at Matt's place my fraternity brothers recognized me.

"Hall. Dude. Is that you? It is you. Man, I hardly recognized you. How you feeling?"

"Pretty good."

"What have you been up to?"

"Not much, really."

"Killer. Can't believe you're back. We've got to get together. Do some partying. Give me a call. Come by the house. We'll hit up Manny's, Kip's, the City, the Triangle, Dunk-ball in the afternoon. Get you running around, have you doing the town in no time. Call me."

I didn't call. Left Matt's place a day later. Decided to kick those girls out after all, or my new roommate did. He got tired of waiting, too. We no longer cared about the arrangement my previous roommate made. School was starting in three days. We needed to get settled in, bunkered down. The first day of classes meant mayhem. We wanted to be ready.

The first day of class came like a coup. Panicked people pushing, rushing, running this way and that. So little time, so much to do: crashing classes; buying books, paper, pencils; picking up forms to add and drop classes;

dropping off forms to change the grading option of the classes you already had from a letter grade to pass/not pass and vice versa; paying registration; paying late registration; paying previous semesters' registration past due, so you can pay late registration, because your current registration was blocked. So little time, so much to do. Footsteps falling faster, faster. Don't want to be late — late for an important date.

Left my apartment early Monday morning. I needed to crash several classes. As a senior, I should have been given priority over the younger students and received every class I applied for. But, the gods/dogs of scheduling placed me in the re-enrolled students category. When my class confirmation schedule arrived in the mail, they not only denied me all my classes, they weren't even sure of my major — "Undeclared" my schedule read.

I was pissed. Though I felt pretty good, I wasn't sure if I could handle the added stress of crashing four to five classes per day. Wasn't sure if I would have the energy, the patience, the time. Would have been so easy to have my classes laid out for me. I could stroll in like a Fat Cat to a four-course meal, utensils in hand, the right books in my pack, sit down and start picking my way through the Rhetoric, devouring the Economics, with perhaps a little sprig of Environmental Studies on the side.

By the end of the first week I successfully added four classes. By the end of the second, I dropped down to two. I just wasn't quite healthy enough to carry a full load. Found myself sleeping in one class to recoup my energy so I could attend the next. The things one normally takes for granted in the course of a school day became hurdles for me. The walk down the hill to attend class. The walk back home. The walk between buildings, one class to the next. Stopping at the student store to pick up a new book, a new notepad, an organizer; stopping at the copy store, the drugstore. Concentrating for an hour-and-a-half lecture period, taking notes, and following the discussion, so I could ask relevant questions. Meeting with friends, teachers, teacher's aides, study groups. Long days in the library combing through references for a term paper on ... Long nights reading lengthy assignments for timely discussions on pertinent topics in related fields of ... Not to mention all the energy that goes into fulfilling one's basic survival needs — grocery shopping, laundry, folding laundry, cooking dinner, cleaning the dishes you use to cook and eat dinner. I needed more energy for these things that take energy. I needed more time for these things that take time.

For eight months I lived in a sheltered environment, the boy in a plastic bubble. This was a giant leap back into the mainstream, the perpetual scream, screaming from one moment to the next, accomplishing tasks in a perpetual mess. I knew I would have to take it easy, take it slow, take it one day at a time. So, while I was disappointed I didn't quite feel healthy enough to carry a full load, I felt lucky to be back in school, walking the streets, perusing the shops. Mocha in the morning. Shoes without socks. I was a student again, returning to the temple of my familiar.

In the world of roommates, you find two kinds of people: those that bring fun, and those that bring none. At this stage in my life, I wasn't much of a party-er. Didn't even drink. So, I'm not talking party fun, or even person fun. I'm talking gadget fun. The kind of roommate whose appliances compliment your living arrangement. John brought fun. Our appliances complimented one another's perfectly. He had a Denon sound system, with six-foot speakers, and pile of CD's that stretched the living room. I had a computer and dot-matrix printer. He had a VCR with four heads. I had a twenty-inch remote control television set. He had a microwave. I had a blender, dishes, and a wok. He had an all-terrain mountain bike. I had an all-terrain four-by-four 1972 International Scout II with a removable top. From our rooftop apartment you could see the campus, Memorial Stadium, the International House, the Campanile, Oakland, San Francisco, the Golden Gate Bridge with the Pacific Ocean in the distance. The building we lived in was a dump, but we lived in style.

John was one of my teammates. He played four-man, otherwise known as lock in the scrum. I bring this up because we appeared an unlikely duo. He was big — huge, really. Six-feet-five, two hundred and fifty pounds of raw muscle. He was clean-cut, liked hanging with sorority babes in midnight bars. I was skinny and frail. I had a beard, long hair, liked wearing cut-offs. Cut myself off from the frat-scene. Not suggesting the frat-scene was bad, my non-scene better. It was just that I had done that, been there, buyer beware. Didn't share the same ideas I held when I was an "active" member in my previous "incarnation."

Still, we shared a lot of common interests. For one thing, we became good friends through rugby. The fact that I wasn't working out with the team and wasn't even sure whether or not I would play the coming spring did not change that. We still talked about the upcoming season, although at times I felt strange talking about it. Didn't really feel I was a part of the team anymore. I had been away only one season, yet there seemed to be an entirely different group of guys playing. And when I looked into the mirror, I saw someone skinny, frail — a peaceful meditator — everything but a first team scrumhalf.

In a way, John was my connection to the life I had been cast from. The life I was moving away from. I enjoyed hearing his stories, like memories from a distant past. Enjoyed hearing his glories: satisfying workouts on warm fall days ... late nights ... the white knight that rescued the damsel in distress from the drooling drunk, only to become a drooling drunk himself. It all rang close to home. Made me feel I wasn't alone, because those I played and partied with were all still around. Part of me wished I could play and party, too. But I understood the importance of taking it slow, one day at a time — just a day at a time.

For John, I think I represented an extension of his spiritual side that wanted to step away from the well-beaten path of his comfortable life. Much like me, he was raised in an upper-middle class home in southern California. At Berkeley, he found his niche with a team of athletes and fraternity guys who shared his interests in sports and a good education; shared his interests in having a beautiful wife, a beautiful house, and a beautiful car. And yet, he sat up late at night, listening to music, recounting his day. Lights off. Room dark. Something was missing. Some part of him empty. I could see it in his eyes. Could see it in the way he stared out into the room, as if wondering, "How did I get here? Where am I going?"

It wasn't as if he envied me. He knew what I was going through, knew the extent of my fatigue first hand. The way I scheduled my entire day around an activity, like going to class, or going to have lunch with a friend. I rested in the morning before I left. I rested in the afternoon once I returned. Sometimes I made choices. If I went to class during the day, I couldn't go out that night.

Instead, I was someone who, through my illness, had stepped beyond the confines of the comfortable life he was familiar with. I was someone no longer held by the structure of peer pressures dictating what was cool and acceptable, and what wasn't. He sat quietly. I meditated. He stretched. I did yoga. I was in many ways strange or estranged, and by living with me, John shared in my estrangement. By living with me, John could experience the other side of comfortable, without relinquishing the lifestyle to which he had long grown accustomed.

My health improved rapidly. During the first few weeks of the semester, I focused all my efforts into simply attending my two classes. They fell one right after the other on Tuesdays and Thursdays. Each class lasted an hour-and-a-half. Each class demanded my full attention. Sometimes I paid attention. Sometimes I didn't. Sometimes I just closed my eyes, let time wash by, as I listened to the murmur of voices in the room, the sound of lead scratching paper.

Mondays and Fridays were days I basically spent resting, feet up, book open for some light reading. Or perhaps some studying in the morning, with a lazy afternoon listening casually to my roommates' endless collection of CD's that spread the gamut of listener tastes — new age, classical, jazz, funk, grunge, 80s techno-pop, hip-hop, rock. In the evenings I frequently enjoyed a post-dinner guitar jam on the rooftop of my apartment, watching the sun go down.

I spent Saturdays exploring the Bay Area — places I had never seen before, or places I had seen, but wanted to visit again. I took drives over to the north side of Berkeley to sit and strum my guitar in the rose garden on Elm Street, and out to Tiburon for lunch with friends. We'd sit and watch the sail boats, sails flying, hulls splitting-spitting water in their wake, sea gulls gliding. We're all laughing, eating guacamole.

By mid-October, I improved to the point I no longer needed to be so careful; so pedantically conscious of my health — like some modern-day Cinderella gone to the Castle Ball, with two hours of fun before my carriage turns-burns back into a pumpkin.

My biggest breakthrough came when I decided to take a trip to Napa Valley. The parents of my friend Nick, a fraternity brother and former roommate, owned a house there.

"Hall, I'm headed to Napa this weekend. Do you want to come with me?"

"Yeah I do, that sounds like fun."

"Cool, I'll pick you up Friday afternoon. Can you be ready to go at five o'clock?"

"Five o'clock sounds fine. Should I bring anything with me — like food, music?"

"No, we're covered. Just bring clothes, a bathing suit — you know."

"Alright, I'll see you then."

We drove up Friday, listening to reggae on a sound system that pre-dated eight-track, flying through wine country's sobering beauty. Fall was drawing near with the tree leaves changing colors, vines ripe with fruit. From the moment we arrived, we were busy with activities. Ping-pong. Swimming. Diving. On Saturday, we rode bikes around the local vineyards and up through the foothills to the golf and tennis club, where Nick's parents were members. Nick's parents had a couple of friends up, too, and that night we all ate dinner at a Mexican restaurant in town, before returning home to watch *North By Northwest* on video.

Dazed And Fatigued

It was the first time I intentionally stayed up past midnight in over nine months. First time I went through an entire day without a nap, or some other form of rest to break up the day. First time I actually let myself enjoy the moment without worrying at every turn what the consequences might be. First time I felt free in a long, long time.

One of the first things I noticed, while back at Cal, was that my attitude towards school was different. I felt lucky to be back, learning and taking classes on my own terms. Not doing it to please my parents, or appease the system that says take this, study that, get these grades, then enter the parade as an accountant, investment banker, pre-med, post-grad, pencil-pushing porcupine. Do these things and everything everyone ever told you was important and valued in life, you will attain.

Things weren't like that for me anymore. I was in school, because I wanted to learn. Hungry for knowledge of any kind, I searched the local papers for small plays or lectures I could attend. I went to classical music recitals every Friday. Students from the music school playing in duets, trios, violin and flute ensembles in D. Ensembles with piano, cello and clarinet in C minor. Didn't really know what it all meant, nor did I recognize the tunes. But I enjoyed the music, my weekly infusion of culture, and became the philistine who found Beethoven, Bach, and Brahms.

I flew home for Thanksgiving vacation. Before my mom picked me up from my Alaska Airlines flight at Burbank Airport, I stood, bags at my feet, waiting by the baggage claim turnstiles. I remember standing next to a younger guy who was in my house, someone I didn't know too well.

"You know, when I first met you," he said to me as we stood waiting for our rides, "I didn't really like you."

"Oh yeah," I said, "why's that?"

"I just saw you as this wild obnoxious frat-guy. You've really changed, mellowed out a lot."

"Well, it probably wasn't by choice, but thanks."

34

The Fall

Thanks for not saying you used to be this. Or you used to be that.

The summer before I returned to school, I ran into a friend I worked with in Washington D.C. the previous summer. She looked uncomfortable, almost frightened by my appearance. Her hug was terse, her hello even more so. We ran into each other as she made her way with her mom into Bullock's.

"What happened?" she asked.

"I've been sick," I said.

I'm not saying she was wrong to react the way she did. If our situations were reversed, I probably would have reacted the same way, said the same thing with an uneasy smile, and with similar gestures, made a quick goodbye.

At the airport that day, my fraternity brother didn't ask me what happened, or why I thought I'd changed. He heard about it, at least bits and pieces from some of the other guys in our house. We didn't really get into what I went through and I made no effort to discuss the knowledge and wisdom I felt I gained. We didn't even talk for long, because my mom pulled up shortly after I arrived. He just asked me what my plans were for Thanksgiving vacation. He said, "It's been good seein' you." He smiled and slapped me five, then at length, we said goodbye.

*C*hapter 4

I've heard so many stories of people who have experienced severe illness. Perhaps a brush with death, a heart attack, car accident, cancer. The experience changes their lives and they say things like:

"I enjoy life one day at a time now."

"I take time out for the little things."

"I take time out for family and friends; time I took for granted before."

A window has opened up inside their hearts. A window so wide, a man whose only passion was money, starts dedicating his weekends to preserving the Florida Everglades. A woman, once angry at the world, spends weeknights spreading God's word door-to-door in a campaign to "save" the masses.

Warms your heart to see the change, the peace in their faces, the passion, the generosity of spirit, their commitment to giving. Sometimes they carry it for a day — handouts to the homeless, hugs for friends, appreciation for the new chance at life they've been granted. They may carry it for a month, even a year, and if they are lucky — a lifetime.

I found this state of peacefulness. My heart was generous, because it was rich with compassion, my spirit light, because it was buoyant with appreciation for life. Every step I took was fresh, every bite sweet. I felt one with God. God was one with me.

Over Thanksgiving, my mom and I went to see the Picasso exhibit at the Los Angeles County Museum of Art.

While there, I ran into Cameron, my high school girlfriend — the one who brought me her guitar — and her family. Gave her a big hug, her sister a squeeze, her mom a friendly peck on the cheek — definitely family day at the museum. I had been part of their family for a while. During my senior year of high school, I spent more time at their house than mine.

"How are you?" Cameron said.

"I'm good," I said.

"You look great. Hardly recognized you. Love your beard. Very sophisticated."

"Thank you."

"Here for the Picasso exhibit?"

"Yes."

"Us too. Who are you here with?" she said.

"My mom. She's standing right over there."

"Oh, hi, Ms. Hall."

"Hi, Cameron."

"So, good to see you," she said turning back to talk to me. "Can't get over how healthy you look. We'll talk some more inside the exhibit."

"Sure. I'll see you inside."

I saw other friends on that vacation as well. The friends who had not seen me since my illness started, were very surprised by my change in appearance — my lighter frame, my bearded face. When we talked about my illness, we did so as an episode from my past, laid to rest like a relationship with an old lover relevant only as a memory.

Fallen hero washed across a twenty inch screen. He slit her throat. No he didn't. Opposing sides, opposing screams. Take us for a ride, we revel in the tragedy. Take us for a ride, we revel to watch the fallen celebrity. Take us for a ride. Take us for a ride. Take us for a ride. We want to be ridden. So, anywaywayway ... I returned to school at the end of Thanksgiving vacation to take my finals, finish out the semester. I felt confident in my health. More confident than at any time since the onset of my illness the previous fall.

37

Beyond merely finishing out the semester, I felt I was returning to close out a chapter in my life, the battle to regain my health already won. All I needed to do was sign the treaty and make things official.

Perhaps I was a little ahead of myself, a little ahead of reality. I still wasn't entirely healthy. I could basically do everything I wanted — work out, go out, attend classes. But I still felt some part of me not right, my body chemistry slightly awry.

I had, for the previous few months, effectively built my own reality, believing I could attend school, when I wasn't sure whether or not I could; believing I could attend classes, live on my own, run, lift weights, go out to dinner and then to the theater. All these things I achieved, because I believed in myself. In my mind, believing I was totally healthy was merely an extension of that which I already achieved.

I started to think about the spring semester and about the upcoming rugby season. I needed to be faster, stronger. I needed to be in better shape if I wanted to compete. I was still underweight. Gaining ten pounds in a couple months would be difficult, but I felt I could do it. At least I had to try. Playing rugby represented that last hurdle in my recovery, the final plateau reflecting the fact I was physically healed.

I called up one of my friends on the track team. "Hey Brent, this is Mark."

"What's up Hall-bo?"

"I want to start training again and I was wondering if you'd show me some of the exercises you do in practice that build up speed and endurance."

"I could meet you down at the track Saturday morning."

"Great, what time?"

"Ten o'clock?"

"I'll see you there." Brent was a decathlete and I was hoping he could help me put together a program or regimen I could use to base my training on during the upcoming winter break.

We met that Saturday at the track stadium, a classic fall day, the sky clear, the air crisp. Other athletes were training in the stadium that day, too — sprinters, a couple high hurdlers and Jeff, another friend of mine.

"Hall-bo, what's up? What are you doing down here?" Jeff said, confused to see me in sweats and running shoes at the track.

"I'm meeting Brent down here. He's going to take me through a couple drills."

"Cool. Don't work out too hard."

"I won't," I said smiling, just as Brent walked up.

"What's up, Jeff?" he said.

"What's up Brent?"

"Ready Hall-bo? Let's start out by doing a little stretching," Brent said. "Then we can warm up with a few exercises to build up fast twitch muscles. How does that sound? Good?"

"Let's do it," I said.

No one was jumping that day, so we stretched back next to the high-jumpers pit, the grass still wet from early morning precipitation.

After warming up, Brent said, "Now let's run some hundreds, work on form and technique, then we'll call it a day."

"All right. You know, I appreciate you coming out here with me today, Brent. This is going to be a big help."

"Oh, don't even mention it. You ready?"

"I'm ready."

At the end of the workout, I felt tired but invigorated. Over the next week I worked on some of the things Brent showed me. At the same time, the final grind towards finals was on. Spent much of my time researching a paper I was writing for my Rhetoric class. The paper was on Ludwig Wittgenstein's, *Blue and Brown Books*, possibly the driest, most complicated philosophical work I ever read. My task: compare any two paragraphs from the text and explain how one was relevant to the other. Two paragraphs, that was it! Easy, right?

Yet, I was baffled, as were most of my classmates. The book describes a series of language games, breaking language down to the lowest possible denominator. Wittgenstein postulates how one might teach an individual to speak with words or count with numbers given that individual had never seen, heard or spoken using words or numbers before. Probably read Rudyard Kipling's *Jungle Book* once too often as a child.

After hours of contemplation and studying, reading and re-reading the text, I figured out what my angle would be, then took a moment to congratulate myself on my ingenuity, my insight — Wyle E. Coyote: "Super Genius."

Started writing my paper Sunday afternoon, two weeks before my Economics final, a week-and-a-half before the paper was due. Didn't want to rush through it. I was pacing myself. I was ahead of the game.

The Friday before, I clearly overdid my workout. I was tired and frustrated that I felt tired, because it wasn't a healthy tired. It was a fuzzy tired. The kind of tired that reminded me I still wasn't completely healthy. After all I went through, the gains I made, I still wasn't completely healthy. I could still feel *fuzzy tired*. Why couldn't my illness just fade?

Pressure from school. Pressure I put on myself to be healthy and get into shape. Pressure so that I started feeling, "I may never be totally better." Just a thought, a fear, something even I knew wasn't true. But, it made me anxious.

Determined to prove to myself I was okay, I decided to attend my yoga class. I walked down to my friend's apartment two flights down to see if he wanted to go with me. Down the cement stairwell with its plaster-cracked walls, loose handrails — one end hanging, or fallen altogether. No light — a safety-fire hazard — the entire building was a hazard. Should have been condemned years ago.

I knocked on his door. No answer. I knocked again. No answer. Started to walk away when he opened the door. He clearly wasn't going. Hung over — and most likely still drunk — from the night before. Manny's something, something ... Henry's something, something ... eight shots, seven beers something, something. I promised to tell him what he missed. He closed the door. I walked back down the hall, then further down the stairs to Bancroft Avenue. I was more determined than ever to do my yoga with or without him.

40

Two hours of stretching, posing, hand stands, and back bends. I walked back to my apartment sore and dehydrated, but feeling pretty good. I was tired, but it was healthy tired. My fuzzy tired faded with the Berkeley morning fog. Sun was out. Sat out on my rooftop sipping minestrone soup from a stoneware mug.

While my fuzzy tired faded, my anxiety didn't. It stirred, brewed, and churned like a kettle brought to boil. I tried reading to get my mind off my fears. But my incessant paranoia kept needling me: *You're never going to get better.* Why am I so tired? *You're never going to get better.* Why am I so tired?

I started thinking maybe I should just go for a little bike ride, burn some steam. I was feeling pretty good. Maybe I should go pick up a honey dew melon from the store — something sweet, a tasty, juicy, dripping treat.

And then I was going. Put down my things, grabbed my bike, pushed it out the front door, onto the elevator, out into the foyer of my apartment building, and into the street. I was coasting down Bancroft, fresh wind on my face, my spirit free.

I pedaled down College Avenue, stopped at the vegetable market across from Safeway, and picked out a choice honey dew melon. It was firm, but you could squeeze it. The ends smelled sweet, ripe — the perfect melon. I put it in my pack and prepared to climb back on my bike to ride home.

And yet, my restlessness burned. I tapped into something far greater than anxiety or fear. I tapped into rage: rage against myself, hatred for not being well, not being able to do the things I wanted, or feel the way I wanted to feel.

In that moment, I lost touch with all sense of compassion and caring for myself, instead of being understanding, recognizing that my suffering led me to this state of virtual hysteria. I am not a crazy man, a man beyond control or reason. In that instant there was no reason. All the anger I projected on the world — the "why me" anger, the "it's not fair" — turned inward. Like a boy brought up in an abusive home who turns his anger at the world upon himself and takes his own life. I didn't go that far. I would never go that far, but the mechanism is the same.

I climbed back on my bike, wrapping my hands in a firm grip around the handle-bars; squeezing so hard, my knuckles turned white. I didn't take the easy way home, the casual ride back up College Ave., past the shops and sorority houses, past the dorms, Units One and Two. I took Claremont — the slow, hard climb — and went after it. I pedaled fierce, legs pumping, teeth clenched, my butt high over the seat so I could really dig into the climb. Consciously, I was going to conquer the hill. But subconsciously, I think I had set out to conquer myself. By the time I got to Piedmont Avenue, my lungs ached, and fluids streamed down my face.

Back at my apartment I took a hot shower, toweled off, and settled into the synthetic leather brown bean bag nestled in the corner of our living room. Exhausted, I knew I overstretched my bounds ... I just didn't know how far. So, I spent the following day lounging around the apartment, reading and watching TV.

By Sunday I felt a little better, not much, but a little. Knew I needed to start writing my paper. Knew I needed to buy groceries for the following week. It was crunch time in Berkeley and I had to be prepared — cupboards stocked with food. By the time I made it to the library, it was mid-afternoon. My head throbbed, a headache flaring. Just wanted to get a few hours of writing in before the library closed.

I took out my textbook, paper, pens, and scribble notes, which I scattered all around me, only to realize I couldn't study. Couldn't even focus. Why did I come down here at all? I packed up my things and started walking home. My apartment was just up the hill, but it seemed miles away. Felt like I wasn't going to make it. As I stepped out of the elevator, my head was spinning, feet heavy on the tar-covered roof, the walkway to my apartment.

That night I called my dad. I was crying on the phone. My next-door neighbor stopped by, saw me crying and asked, "What's wrong, Mark? You don't look too good."

"Nothing," I said. "I'm just tired." But I knew what was wrong. I had relapsed again.

The Fall

Spent the next several days in bed. For a while I fought it, half writing to finish my paper, half sleeping, thinking there might be some way to take my Economics final. I even arranged it to the point so all I needed to do was answer one question verbally during my Economics professor's office hours. He offered to grade my response in lieu of a final examination.

I tried to study, but there was no way. I could barely keep my eyes open. So, I took an Incomplete — wouldn't take a grade I didn't deserve. Flew home two weeks later, three days before Christmas. Wanted to return home in triumph, to end my semester with a bang. But, as I lay down on my bed in Los Angeles, my head in turmoil, legs still weary from my flight, all I could do was whimper.

Part 2:

The Wilderness

Chapter 5

A brown shoe. A white room. On the second story. Of my mom's gray house. A small yard. A tree-lined street. In Los Feliz Hills. The happy hills. Overlooking Los Angeles. Sprawled-out city. On the Pacific Coast. West of the Sierras. Where the desert meets the sea. A divided country. Separated by race, wealth, region and religion. On a continent. In the northern hemisphere. Of a blue planet. Which R. Buckminster Fuller called "Spaceship Earth."

Keep going. Think about Earth, a relatively small planet in our solar system; one of many solar systems in our galaxy — the Milky Way; a crablike spiral filled with globular clusters and nebulous clouds; a galaxy within a universe that curves back upon itself through space and time — the fourth dimension.

I thought about these things for the first time in my senior year of high school. I was taking Astronomy with John Fuelner, science teacher, jazz/fusion guitarist, man on the move. Had a Corvette he loved more than the women he dated. He talked about his Vette every day of the week, every week of the year. Told stories about ladies who mistakenly set their handbags on the hood of his precious car, freshly painted, pearl black.

"So, I had a date Friday night. Went to see a movie. When it was done we walked outside. We were standing next to my car and she puts her purse right on the hood of my Vette. Uuggghh! So I say, 'Would you mind please

47

removing your purse from the hood of my Vette?' She looks at me, as if to say, 'What's the big deal?'" He raised his arms in the air, like a man imitating a bird of prey, shrugged his shoulders, cocked his head the way he always did — to the left, eyes glancing to the right, mouth crooked in disgust:

"I said: 'Well the big deal is that your purse is sitting on the hood of my Vette. You're going to scratch the paint.' Brand new paint job. The nerve of some people. That's the last time I take her out."

In my senior year, I started doing more of what one might call extracurricular partying, smokin' hooch, and drinkin' booze from the craggy bluffs overlooking my school.

One day, I knew we were scheduled to watch a slide show of the planets in our solar system — Mars, Venus, Mercury, Pluto. I remember thinking this the perfect time, since my class started at 8:00, for a little morning bong session, a little wake-and-bake.

I got stoned that morning — really stoned. Thai buds burning in a make-shift bong. Walked into class, sat down, took off my Eddie Bauer pack, closed my eyes, and waited quietly for the show to start.

"Wasn't this a great call," I thought to myself. "Wasn't I cool. Everyone else sitting through this thing sober, watching a cheesy slide show. And here I sit, about to experience the dark side of the moon."

Someone pulled the blinds and dimmed the lights. The projector turned on. A bright white light lit up the silver-backed screen. Mars. Saturn. Uranus. When we got to Jupiter, the largest planet in our solar system, I was awestruck by the shape, the size — eleven times the diameter of the Earth. I stared into its noble gaseous eye, and its noble gaseous eye stared back.

The eye spoke to me, as I started thinking to myself, "Who am I in relation to this massive planet? A massive planet in an even more massive universe, where Jupiter is about the size of a grain of sand drifting on a windswept beach. Where does that leave me? I'm nothing, nobody, nada, inconsequential, a blip in time — a gigablip in time." If a pill made Alice smaller, Jupiter and a bowl of marijuana made me into an infinitesimal speck of dust, clinging just barely onto the hangnail of infinity.

Too much for a stoned teenager to think about. Yet I thought about it often. Is it possible that our entire universe is merely a configuration of atoms, neurons and neutrinos spinning within the confines of a still larger being? And we the Lilliputians inside a Gulliver too large to comprehend? Outrageous! Impossible! Maybe. But if it is true, where then does this new revelation leave me? How valuable could my life possibly be? Does any of this bullshit we have come to revere — luxurious trips, accomplished career, the adulation of our peers — have meaning and worth? Or are we just lonely little insects building bridges on an afterthought — Earth?

Digressions. Digressions. Depression. Let's get back to the story. Back from the outer reaches of our puzzling universe. Back across space and time, through distant galaxies. Watch your step, you're slipping into a black hole — gravity and light collapsing in on itself. Don't want to end up in the Twilight Zone. Back through the Milky Way. On into our unique little solar system. Past Pluto and Neptune. Past Jupiter and Saturn. Back to Earth. To our northern hemisphere. The United States. West of the Mississippi. West of the Sierras. To California. And finally, back to my modern industrial style home, the home our real estate broker Al never sold, perched high in the Los Feliz Hills overlooking Los Angeles — the City of Angels.

Sitting around my southern California home that Christmas, I once again lost faith in my ability to cure myself. To make it so far, so near to having my health restored, only to be slick-slack, slapped back to the point from which I started. I questioned whether I had actually been close to regaining my health at all.

While at school I began playing sports, was able to attend classes, take guitar lessons, take trips with friends ... but the illness was always with me. Don't know how else to explain it other than to say, it was always there, lurking behind my eyes, and in the nether reaches of my brain;

waiting patiently to sneak up on me, if I let my guard down, or became careless, impatient, destructive.

In many ways the illness had been my teacher the previous months. Taught me to have patience, make choices, and have compassion for myself and others. Still, I fought it. I was tired of being patient, compassionate, and grateful for all the things my illness taught me. I was young and felt restless. Paid the price for my restlessness, but was it my fault? I just wanted to be healthy, disease free. There had to be a way. I had to find a cure.

I went to a chiropractor in Beverly Hills, a posh office with an anatomically correct couch supposedly great for your back, though it was hell to sit on. The waiting room was decorated in Japanese motif — bamboo shoots and Bonsai trees, wallpaper with waterfowl stenciled in gold trim.

I started seeing him four times a week for a month. "I'm cleaning your onion," he told me. "Layers of physical, emotional and spiritual blocks built up in your body over a lifetime of struggle have left you weary, tired."

On my first visit, he asked me to write down the names of people who may have hurt me in the past, caused deep emotional pain — family members, friends, coaches, teachers. The people I trusted most, because those we trust always hurt us the most. We give them love, love they may not give back, or if they do, give it back in hurtful ways — obsessive love, jealous love, retaliatory love. It could be something less intentional. Maybe they're not trying be cruel at all. Maybe they're just tired, or had a bad day. The car broke down. Boss chewed them out at work.

It doesn't matter, the result's the same. We run to them with open arms and they brandish their sword, razor-edged stares, a tongue sharp like slashing steel. They cut us up, rip us to shreds. We stand there and take it — all the condescension and criticism. Yet we wonder why they're doing this. Why they're acting this way. How they could be so cruel.

Cruelty is in our nature, an integral part of us all. Look around. Witness famine, disease, natural selection, the balance between predator and prey — nature's way of eliminating the weak, so the strong can survive.

There is no excuse for abuse or undue cruelty, but we have all been cruel at one time or another. Some more than others. None of us are saints. Makes sense that those we love injure us the most. By opening ourselves up to love, we instantly open ourselves to hurt.

With names of my family and friends scrawled and numbered on a piece of paper I held in my hand, my chiropractor began to ask yes or no questions of my body. Questions of incidents locked inside my body. If the answer was yes, my right leg became visibly longer than my left. If the answer was no, my left leg became visibly longer than my right. Strangest thing I ever saw.

"Is the name of the person on the list?"

Yes.

"Is it between the numbers one and five?"

No.

"Six and ten?"

Yes.

"Is it six?"

No.

"Seven?"

No.

"Eight?"

Yes.

"When did the incident occur? Was if between the ages of one and five?"

No.

"Six and ten?"

No.

"Eleven and fifteen?"

No.

"Sixteen and twenty?"

Yes.

The process happened quickly. When the person and time period were discerned, he would ask me to recall the incident. Sometimes I couldn't, but usually I could. He asked me to picture the incident, picture the person's face at the time the incident occurred, stare into their eyes and forgive them for the pain they caused me; ask them to

51

forgive me for any pain I might have caused them; forgive myself for the pain I caused myself.

After each person had been forgiven, he asked, "Is there anything more you would like to forgive?"

If my body responded "yes," we continued; "no," and the session was over.

I slowly started feeling better, but it was subtle. Couldn't tell if I was just getting better on my own, or if my chiropractor was really helping me. Many of the other programs I tried made me worse, yet the doctors would say, "Don't worry, my patients frequently get worse before they get better."

I did worry, because I seldom got better.

This program wasn't like that. Felt stronger every day. No phantom pains, or banking on sunshine when all I got was rain. I stuck with it, and recovered to the point of being able to return to school in time for the spring semester.

I packed my things and returned to Berkeley in late January, with the intent of finishing out my degree — needed just two more classes plus completion credits in the courses I did not complete the previous semester. Grey clouds hovered and lingered, pouring cold, wet rain as I made my way down to campus three times a week.

My chiropractor arranged to have me see a similar practitioner in San Francisco, whom I saw twice a week. Kept my raincoat buttoned to the chin, my umbrella close in tow, and things went smoothly the first few weeks at school.

Yet, as the semester heated up, my confidence quickly dissipated. A couple days feeling tired and I began to question my ability to attend classes — flashbacks to previous semesters tried and failed. I wondered how long I would last, how soon until I'd crash.

Went home a couple days to regain my footing. Talked to my former therapist, Michelle. She could help me. She would know what to do. She would help me regain my confidence. And she did.

"So, how are things going up at school, Mark?"

"I don't know. Guess I just don't feel safe. Like I'm standing on thin ice and it's about to give."

"Are you afraid you might relapse? How do you feel right now?"

"I feel okay. It's just that it's already happened a couple times."

"What's happened?"

"I've relapsed in the past, feeling better than I do now. There's a lot going on up at school and I'm afraid it may happen again."

"Do you want to withdraw?"

"No."

"Well, it sounds like you're just feeling a little overwhelmed. Are you seeing anyone, like a therapist or a counselor at school?"

"No."

"Maybe you should. And in the meantime, just do the best you can. If you don't feel up to doing something, don't do it. Take the day off and take care of yourself."

"Okay."

It worked for about two weeks, until I caught my first cold and was left flat on my back in my one-bedroom apartment on the coldest week that winter. Could barely get out of bed to make soup. My nose was stuffed up, my head pounded.

Wasn't my cold that forced me to withdraw one week later, it was my history. I just wasn't emotionally prepared to deal with the ups and downs. With each misstep, I panicked, questioned, wondered. School was the farthest thing from my thoughts, when all my thoughts were focused on how I was or wasn't feeling. The fear, uncertainty and stress were more than I could bear. So, I picked up the phone and called home: "Can you send me a plane ticket Mom? I want to come back."

The next few months were like a roller coaster ride — up one week, down the next. Can't say if my moods were driving my health, or if my health was driving my moods. Up one week, down the next. Up. Down. Up. Down. A day-glo yo-yo stuck spinning on an eighteen-inch string.

Stopped seeing my chiropractor, because the treatment wasn't really helping me.

53

"You have to be patient. These things take time."
But I had no patience. Time was passing me by.
I returned to my Berkeley apartment, because I wanted to
stay in the loop as best I could. Back home was comfortable,
peaceful, safe, but it was boring — a quiet neighborhood,
on a quiet street, people hiding behind large whitewashed
walls, taking refuge from the city below. Sometimes I
went days without seeing another person other than my mom.

In Berkeley, I liked knowing I could walk outside and
see people. Laying in the soft grass outside Wurster Hall,
I watched other students walking to campus, jogging,
biking, skating; people with packs and books, books in
packs. I could be anonymous, a face in the crowd, and at
the same time take in the life that radiated all around.
Spring had arrived, the sun once again shined.

I started reading voraciously. In Ayn Rand's, *The
Fountainhead*, I learned about a different kind of hero —
Howard Roarke. Unlike most heroes, Roarke is a selfish
man, an under appreciated outcast. Yet, we revere him for
his belief in himself, his unwillingness to compromise his
ideas, or suck up to the status quo just so he can be recognized. The only thing that matters to him is the truth —
Roarke's truth. While he seems cold, callous, we respect
him, because his actions are untainted by outside
influences. We respect him for his commitment to succeed
on his own terms.

I read about other heroes, both fictional and real. More
of Shakespeare's tragic heroes, heroes from the classics
like Odysseus, Socrates and Plato, Hercules — half man,
half god.

Reading Joseph Campbell's *Hero with a Thousand
Faces*, I became fascinated by the concept of the hero's
journey. A journey that begins by falling from a life that is
comfortable and familiar, into wilderness. A liminal
space, where the hero is stripped of his/her previous
position of rank or authority. In this liminal space the hero
experiences a journey, and in the process undergoes a
period of learning that expands the hero's mind and soul.
Little bits of knowledge, fragments of wisdom ... pieces
that, when the hero returns from the wilderness, no longer

resemble the barbed fragments of the unconscious, but nuggets of pure gold that can make a man a prophet, a woman a saint.

I read these stories for a couple hours each day in the cafes along Bancroft and Telegraph Avenue. In the evening I played my guitar, spent time on the phone talking with friends, and dubbed recordings off my roommate's CD collection.

Yet I still wasn't improving. While at school, I wasn't attending classes or student functions. I was an outsider, not a participant. Each day that passed, I felt further separated from campus life, the life I aspired, and became more and more frustrated. But, where could I go? There had to be someplace for me to escape my malaise. Woke up crying one night and stumbled out onto my balcony. Scattered lights littered the bay. Reach out to me ... is there something you want to say? If only I were a prophet or a saint.

The semester ended and I knew I would have to return home to Los Angeles, only to face more long days, lonely nights — something I wasn't willing to do. Needed a new journey to expand my mind, a fresh mind to expand my journey. I was tired, but restless like one of those Mexican jumping beans. Had to get out and escape my scene. My non-scene. Me.

*C*hapter 6

I boarded the Air Canada mid-morning flight from Los Angeles to Toronto and it reminded me of journeys I had taken in the past — windowed terminals, fluorescent lights, the cafeteria with day-old food kept warm under an orange heat lamp, smiling faces of friendly ticket takers, stepping though the gate and walking down the carpeted ramp onto the wide-bodied plane.

It reminded me of my boyhood, at five or six years old, flying to spend the long hot summers with my grandparents in Michigan. A change from my routine in Los Angeles. A change I looked forward to for months, to spend time with my uncles, cousins, and friends who lived in the neighboring houses, on neighboring streets, in a neighborly suburb of Warren.

It reminded me of the summer I flew to Washington D.C. to work as an intern on Capitol Hill. Six college guys living in a townhouse, four doors up from the corner of 30th and Q Street in Georgetown.

Flying was a way to experience new adventures, tackle new domains. But it was also a way to run away and escape a complicated situation for which no other solution seemed viable. So it reminded me of the trip I took to Europe, the summer after my freshman year at Berkeley:

I totaled my car towards the end of my senior year in high school, driving one drunken afternoon — smash, thud, face through the windshield of my red Rabbit two-door. Blood. Tears. Crying hysterically in the back

56

of a speeding ambulance, my blood alcohol level so high the doctor asked to have me arrested. I wasn't, but my car was gone, my insurance canceled. My parents weren't paying my way to drive any more.

After a year of college and the freedom that comes with being away from home, I didn't want to go home to Los Angeles and the cage of living under my parents' roof, in a city where a car is the only viable means of transportation.

"You can take the bus."

"You can ride a bike."

"You can always walk."

"Walk? Get real. My friends live all over town. And nobody takes the bus, unless they're too young to drive, or too poor to afford a car."

Go ahead, chastise me as an elitist. Yet this is the sad legacy of a city ruined by monoliths of a bygone era, who wanted to sell tires, automobiles, and buses to anyone who bought into their bullshit that a car meant freedom, status, and the path to a brighter future.

Well, I bought in — my freedom/status squandered on a Mira Costa roadside; I chose not to go home that summer. Instead I was going to ride the steel rails of Europe using my two-month Eurail pass; going to kick back in the South of France and the small beach towns and fishing villages that lined the Amalfi Coast; going to Berlin — the Wall and Checkpoint Charlie before they fell down; going to Amsterdam — the red light district, space cakes, the Miro, check out all the six-foot blond babes riding on bikes too fast to ask, "Hey! Where are you headed?"

My dad picked me up from the airport. I was tired and weary from the long flight, but it was good to see him. Hadn't seen him since the previous summer, the week before I returned to school.

"How are you feeling?" he said.

"I'm doing alright," I said.

"How was your flight?"

"It was alright."

"Did you sleep on the plane?"

"Yeah. Listened to tunes. Watched the movie. Slept."

"What was the movie?"
"Can't remember. It was that one with ..."
"Was it any good?"
"It was alright."

Dad lived in a one-room bachelor apartment on Lascalles Boulevard just west of Yonge Street in the center of Toronto. He lived a relatively simple life, partly by choice, partly by circumstance.

He separated from his second wife six months before. He called it a "temporary" arrangement, until they could work out their differences. In the meantime, he was finding himself to figure out why his marriage wasn't working out; why his life wasn't going the way he wanted it to go; why, even though he followed the path set out for him by his parents and by society — a path to success, happiness, peacefulness — he could not find any of them in his life.

He moved to Canada my sophomore year of college to marry the woman he was at this point separated from. They met at a dinner party through a mutual friend, started dating, and chose to get married a year later.

"What are you thinking about," I said at the time, "you barely even know her." I remember being angry when he told me he was leaving Los Angeles. Even though I was away at college, I experienced feelings of abandonment, as if his leaving meant he would no longer be there to support me.

At the same time, I felt he was running away from problems in his personal life. Problems so confusing, so long mishandled, I couldn't believe he got himself into them. But who was I to judge? Criticize. Second guess. Nothing I could do to clean up his slip-drag mess.

A successful architect in Los Angeles, he tried to open up a branch of his firm in Toronto. His business partners didn't want him to go. Told him he couldn't go. He went anyway — went, because he was running away. Negotiations. Legal disputes. The company dissolved in a bitter battle, each party demanding justice. Demanding equity. Demanding. Demanding.

After a rapid progression of lawyer's fees, unkept promises, and bad investments, my father lost everything

within about two years. His marriage ended shortly thereafter. He was camping out in an apartment the size of a
small dining room, wondering what hit him.

By the time I arrived, my dad was starting to put his
life back together again. Had a good job, earning good
money, though he wasn't thrilled to be working for someone
else. And though most of what he made went to pay off
debt, it gave him time to find himself; to search for
answers to questions he too long forsook. He did individual
therapy. Group therapy. He had a men's group he partici-
pated in once a week. On the weekend he did workshops
— Tantric breathing, inner child discovery. His was an
obsessive quest for knowledge, a steady flux of journaling,
subconscious probing and analytical self-assessment.
He was a new-age, re-born baby-boomer, the kind they
joke about on TV, except it's never really funny.

Driving the streets back to his apartment from the
airport, I didn't know what to expect. Like my dad before
me, I was running to Toronto because I had no place left to
go; running to find a cure, hoping this place might possess
the magic elixir I sought for so long — sought, though it
eluded me in the States. That this might be the place I
would shatter the manacles of illness which held me captive.

I was running to find my father, the man who moved
away three years before; the man who for years was
estranged to me, as a result of the long drawn divorce
between my parents, where he was always portrayed by
my mother as the bad guy.

I was running, because Canada was something new,
something different. It was an ego thing. Sure it's silly.
But I couldn't just hang out at home, moping, feeling sorry
for myself as the rest of my friends graduated, traveled the
world, spent the summer in Mozambique, only to return
home to some amazing job in Manhattan, Chicago, Tokyo,
London. I was competing in that most ridiculous game of
"I'm so cool. How about you?" In going to Toronto, I
was searching for my niche, trying to be original, trying to
be unique.

When we arrived at his apartment, it was even smaller

59

than I expected, yet surprisingly comfortable. Pictures, sketches, and etchings, bought when my parents lived together in Thailand during the Vietnam War, decorated the room. He had a television and a stereo system neatly stacked away against one wall; a stained oak bookshelf, filled with architectural books, statuettes, and a small collection of turn of the century tools on the wall leading into the kitchen that he had started collecting from antique shops around town.

Windows lined the back of the apartment, where he had hanging pieces of stained glass he made as a hobby in his spare time. The colored glass made the light shine through green, brown, red and cloudy blue onto a white carpet. As I walked across and stepped through the patio door onto the balcony, it seemed as if we were in a tree house. We were on the third floor. Branches extending from tree trunks crept up the balcony rails, where long green flower boxes teemed with plants and a colorful assortment of summer flowers.

I put my things away in a closet he cleared for me. My plan was to stay through the summer, recover my health as quickly as possible, and return to Berkeley for the start of the Fall semester to finish school.

I was being optimistic, based on my experience over the past year. Yet, I figured, if in the period of one week I could get so sick as to have an illness that would last a year, there was nothing that said I couldn't improve to the point of recovery in a period of two months.

Dad and I had a lot of fun that summer. Got to know each other again. On weekdays, I sometimes went to work with him. I hung out in his office and ran short errands, drew, or talked to his secretary, Amanda, who didn't seem to be doing much work anyway and so enjoyed having someone around to pass the time.

Sometimes I just stayed home, walked to the small tree-lined park two blocks from the apartment, lay down in the tall green grass, soaking in sunlight, staring at the sky through the branches of a large maple tree.

The park was a focal point for neighborhood activity

during the summer. I often carried a book with me to read, a notebook to write in. I'd peer out over the pages to watch people walking dogs, who seemed more like family members, friends, lovers than common house pets. Mothers pushing toddlers in strollers to swing the swings. Bikers and joggers getting their daily quota of exercise.

For lunch each day, my dad walked home from work as I prepared a variety of vegetarian soups, salads and sandwiches. We sat out on the small balcony and talked about the way our days were going — the sunshine overhead, the funny people we saw in the park and on the street.

On weekends, my dad showed me around Toronto. We would drive down to Harbour Front to check out the arts and crafts fairs held virtually every weekend of the summer to watch the boats sail out from the marina; have lunch in the crowded pavilions and watch people walking the shops. We'd listen to musicians play their fiddles and banjos on the stone steps outside, trying to earn a buck from the eager crowd of people standing by.

He taught me to make stained glass. "So, what do you want to make?" he asked one day.

"I don't know. What about a purple mushroom with big green spots? Purple and green are my favorite colors."

"Sounds interesting. First you're going to have to draw the pattern, then we'll go out and buy the glass for it."

"All right." So, I drew the pattern. We then browsed the stained glass shop for the glass to fit the pattern I created, and for a project he was working on.

"Now that you've cut the pieces," he said, "you want to start putting it together. What you do is fit the glass into the lead ... here — let me show you."

"How do you keep it from falling apart before soddering?" I said.

"Use these metal pins ... see? Like that."

"Okay, I think I've got it." When I finished, we hung it in front of the large glass window next to his to see what it looked like when the light shone through — opaque magenta, purple, green.

"You do good work," my dad said, scratching his

shaven chin as he stood back to get a better look. "Now, what are you doing for your next project?"

"Some kind of thirties art deco piece maybe. I don't know, I'll have to get back to you on that."

We were two grown men camping out on the floor of his third-story bachelor apartment in a city that for both of us, wasn't quite home. We slept on fold-out mattresses. He was on one side of the room, I was on the other. We often stayed up and talked about the books we read, issues in our lives, my illness, the endless saga of his failing love relationships. My dad was glad to have a companion, and I was glad to have one, too.

Chapter 7

Dad's wife, Gordeen, lived less than a mile from the apartment on Lascalles. A short walk through the park, then three blocks up, and through a second park would take you to the front door of her three-story walk-up apartment.

She lived with her daughter, Charlene, and it was the kind of place you could hang out in, listen to music, watch a little TV, read a book in the oversized blue armchair, and look out the large picture-glass window onto the street below.

I first met Gordeen on my previous visits to Toronto, before my dad's marriage began its downward spiral into dissolution. She was a therapist. An idealist. A woman willing to share her opinions and views to help those who needed help, needed answers to problems for which there are only temporary solutions. In many ways, she helped me.

While they no longer lived together at the time I arrived in Toronto, my dad and Gordeen were still trying to work things out. Through their marriage they tried to bring their children together. Gordeen's daughter and son became my stepsister and brother. Guess it was their way of christening the marriage, so to speak, legitimizing that which probably should not have needed legitimization.

Hit it off first with Charlene, four years younger than myself. We met when I came with my dad to visit Toronto for the first time, before he ever left Los Angeles. We went ice skating together one day. It was winter, but the sun was out over the small outdoor rink down at Harbour

Front. I was terrible. It was my first time. Charlene virtually carried me around the rink.

"I'm so bad at this," I moaned.

"You're doing pretty well," she replied, just as I stumbled, bumbled, like a zamboni gone haywire. By the end of the day my backside was bruised and wet, but we had a great time.

I think I always wanted a little sister or brother. As an only child, I often yearned to have another someone around: someone to share my experiences and be around when problems emerged; someone to count on; someone who would count on me. So, the idea of having a new younger sister appealed to me. Having a new brother did not.

Sean was a year older than myself. He was honest, straightforward — the kind of guy who has no hidden agendas beyond the agenda you see. When we met, his main interests were music, motorcycles, and driving an eighteen-wheel truck from Prince Edward Isle across the continent to the coast of British Columbia.

Wasn't that I didn't like Sean. Like I said, he was a good guy with a kind heart. Or that we didn't get along, because I think we did. Problem was, from the day my dad moved up to Toronto, he was so in need of a stable home life, so eager to establish himself as part of a family unit, that Sean — my stepbrother, who wasn't really my stepbrother, whose own father was to some degree removed from the picture — became my father's "son."

I remember calling my father's office and asking the secretary if I could speak to him.

"Who's calling?"

"His son."

"Is this Sean?"

"No, it's Mark!"

Within a period of a few months, here was this young guy — a guy I barely knew, a guy my dad knew little more than a year — who was getting the same billing I was.

No one ever asked me how I felt about it. My dad certainly didn't. No one ever explained to me the circumstances surrounding the absence of Sean's father that may have helped me to understand why Sean was now my father's son, too.

I was nineteen years old then. A college sophomore. "I didn't think it would bother you that I moved to Toronto," dad told me that summer.

"How could it not?" I protested. "Was I just supposed to accept it? Accept the fact that you were leaving the country with no plans of coming back?"

"You were off in college and had your own life. I was just looking for mine."

That's what happens as you exit your teens — family stability, like a Turkish rug, yanked from beneath your feet. Left me hangin' in midair, until I thunk, pain in my rump, landed on the hardwood floor. Looked up to find my father out the door, high-tailing it to Canada, like some military draft dodger.

Of course I was angry, and for a while I resented Sean. Resented Gordeen. Resented Charlene. I blamed them for having stolen my dad away from me.

As time passed — one year, two years, three — my resentment slowly dissipated. I began to accept my father's new life, the fact he chose to move to Canada. I felt he handled the situation poorly, yet I realized his decision to move had nothing to do with me.

I spent my Monday nights over at Gordeen's place and generally hung out through the following day. My dad dropped me off for dinner. Just because he and Gordeen weren't getting along, we all figured there was no reason I shouldn't maintain my friendship with Gordeen and Charlene.

Charlene still lived with Gordeen. They were very close. When my dad and Gordeen had one of their fights, Charlene understandably tended to side with her mom. If her mom wasn't speaking with my dad, Charlene generally wasn't either.

Sean lived with his girlfriend, Nicole, on the second story of a semi-detached duplex off Yonge Street. He tended to avoid the conflict between my dad and Gordeen altogether, never taking sides. Like Switzerland during war, he positioned himself as a neutral third party.

65

You might say I was trying to foster that role myself. Casual conversations, over casual dinners, in the casual comfort of Gordeen's third-story apartment.

Gordeen was interesting. Over dinner our conversations ranged from current events in Canadian government to recent theories on dreamwork analysis.

"In a few years, before I get too old, I think I'm going to sell everything and travel the country," Gordeen said one night, smiling like someone with a secret to reveal.

"Where do you want to go?" I said.

"I don't know. I'll just start on one side of the country, maybe as far east as Prince Edward Island, and head west."

"Drive cross country. I've always wanted to do that."

"I'm not going to drive, I'm going to walk."

"Across the country?"

"Sure. I'll have a big walking stick, carry my clothes in a backpack, and walk from the Atlantic to the Pacific, like an old lady Gandhi."

"Long way for an old lady Gandhi to walk."

"I know. I'm not going to do it in a week, or even a month. I'll take my time, stopping in towns along the way. Might take me a while, but I'll get there — eventually."

I slept on the floor in the guest bedroom, that was more a sitting room than anything else, and generally woke up the following morning to an empty apartment. Gordeen was at work. Charlene in summer school. In their absence, I became a voyeur, brushing the dust off Gordeen's vinyl music collection, listening to records from a bygone era: *John Denver's Greatest Hits, Credence Clearwater Revival, Dylan, Joan Baez, The Beatles.*

I browsed through the books on Gordeen's maplewood bookshelf; books both interesting and entertaining — from *The Tao of Pooh,* to *Hatha Yoga: diagrammed in the nude.*

I took walks to the park two blocks away. Much like the one near my dad's place, it contained a small athletic field with a playground for kids. Nannies and mothers pushing strollers down the treelined paths. Old men resting on wood benches, watching the nannies and mothers pushing strollers down treelined paths. Kids playing pickle, football, and ultimate frisbee. And me kicking it off to the side, stretched out in the tall grass, watching everyone.

I often waited for Charlene to get home from school. She would be going to university in the fall, which was something she had mixed feelings about.

We would sit in the living room — she in the lounge chair, me on the couch, a table between us — like an interview. I asked her, "Are you excited about going away to school?"

"I'm really excited. I'm looking forward to living in Montreal. Meeting new people."

"Do you know anybody who goes there now? Do you have any friends who will be going to school with you?"

"I know one girl, but we're not really friends or anything. So, I'm a little nervous that I won't know anybody there. My good friends will be hundreds of miles away. You know?"

"Yeah. When I went to Berkeley it was sort of like that. No one from my year was going, but I did know a few people. The key for me was playing sports and joining a fraternity. You've got to join a club or some group you're interested in. You dance, right?"

"Oh yeah."

"See. That's the way to make new friends, so you don't start the year feeling isolated. My first semester, all I did was party. But, I was always bummed, because my high school girlfriend was going to college in Menlo Park. Just an hour away, but I never saw her. When we did, we were uncomfortable — me not knowing what she had been doing, she not knowing what I had been doing ... The first few months were awful. Whatever you do, don't go away to college still dating somebody. Big mistake. You'll spend your entire first semester sniveling on the phone."

As evening approached, Charlene and I would prepare dinner together, then wait for Gordeen to arrive home from work. The pattern was for me to have dinner the second night before my dad came and picked me up to take me back to his place.

Gordeen suggested over dinner one night, I see John Wendt, the therapist both she and my dad saw separately for the past two years. I humored her, saying I would go, but never called to schedule an appointment. And once, I scheduled an appointment, then canceled because I wasn't feeling well, wasn't feeling up to it, was busy, or some other excuse I used to avoid going.

Sitting around my dad's apartment a few weeks later, searching through his music collection, I stumbled across a tape titled, *XMAS 1971 at Grandpa's*. Made me curious. I didn't remember having seen the tape ever before. I put it on and listened.

My grandfather originally made the tape and sent it to my parents — his way of sharing the Michigan Christmas we were unable to attend that year. He had taped the entire family experience, from Christmas eve through Christmas day, on a new tape recorder he bought, interviewing all my relatives, including aunts, uncles, cousins and second cousins.

Been a long time since I heard my grandfather's voice. He died when I was seventeen of bone marrow cancer that spread rapidly through his body and took his life at an early age. Not that early though ... I guess he just seemed young. He was an outdoorsman — loved to fish and hunt. Warm smile, arm around your shoulder.

"How are you doing, Marcus? Fish biting?" he'd say to me.

"Not yet, Grandpa."

"That's okay, son. Just be patient. You'll catch something."

I listened as he described Christmas at their house in Warren. He talked about the tree, Christmas dinner, presents, and who got what from whom. He beckoned my then three-year-old cousin, Sherri Lynn, to speak into the mike. But, she got confused, because she thought the mike was a telephone and she couldn't hear anyone talking on the other end.

"Hello. Hello. Its *Serri*. There's no one there. Who's there? Hello. Hello?"

In the background my uncles played guitar, while the rest of the family sang along to rock classics like, *House of the Rising Sun* and *California Dreaming*.

My grandmother spoke her piece too: "Just wanted you kids to know that you're missed here and that we love you. And we hope that next year you can come and spend Christmas with the family." The same way she does every year and every time we talk. Asks me to come for the fall; or maybe, if I have some time, to visit her during the summer at her place in Kalamazoo. "Maybe some time this year," she says, "you'll find time to visit your old grandma."

As I listened, I found myself transported back in time, sitting in silently with my family. Found myself getting to know these people, not as I remembered them, or how I knew them now, but how they were then, the way they acted, the things they said twenty years before. I sat in on Christmas and the songs they sang, my grandfather speaking to me from across the room through the tape recorder.

"Hope you're having a Merry Christmas, Marcus. I'll see you when you and your parents come driving through here on your way to California this spring."

Then I turned the tape over to the other side. It was the recording my parents sent back to my grandparents of our little family — mom, dad, me — sitting around our apartment in Peabody Terrace, where we lived while my parents attended Harvard grad school. I was around three-years-old at the time, maybe four.

Friday night. In the background, I heard music playing on my parents' stereo. I never actually listened to a tape of myself as a child before. No videos, or home movies — we never made any of those. Just pictures, lots of pictures. I had forgotten what it sounded like to hear my parents when they were younger — when they were still together.

On the recording, we were talking about some photographs my father had taken of our apartment and of Harvard yard. He asked me to describe what I saw:

"And what's this, Mark Mark?" he said.

"That's Mummy and Daddy's house."

"It's not Mark Mark's house?"

"It's my house, too."

As I listened to my voice, listened to what it was like for me to be at home with my parents, sitting in my father's lap, my mother standing just a few feet away,

69

preparing dinner in the kitchen, I started to cry. Tears streamed down my face as I yearned for that which I had lost. Safety. Security. My little family, ripped apart — stolen from me — years before.

I played it over and over again. The same songs in the background. The same words spoken from me and my young family, each time digging deeper into my psyche, until I felt purged. Clean. The tape stopped. Dried my eyes and listened to the quiet drone of the air conditioner, experiencing a new connection with myself — a connection I didn't quite understand, as if the doorway to my inner self, my inner being, had been blown wide open. And in that same instant, I looked inside and saw a pure reflection of myself, untainted by the world outside.

*C*hapter 8

In the will there's a willow where we wayward wanderers walk. Step by step through the quagmire, over the hills and round the block. Up to the palace, see the chalice sitting sterling on the wall. Slip, you stumble, take a tumble, look up to find you've lost it all.

I called John Wendt, the therapist Gordeen had recommended I see, the very next day. Said he had a cancellation later that same week. Said he already talked to my dad about having me come in and that he looked forward to meeting me.

His office was in a large building where several other therapists kept their offices as well. By some architectural blunder the stairwell made it impossible to get to his office without passing through several other offices first. If you entered from the street you could take the stairwell to the first, third and fifth floors. If you wanted to go to the second, fourth and sixth floors, you had to somehow make the journey past two secretaries, four sitting areas, and a series of closed door offices to get to the backside of the stairwell which then took you to the even number floors.

It was very confusing, as you might imagine. Found myself lost on my first few visits, but after a while I got used to it. I wondered how the secretaries ever did:

"Can I help you —"

"Just passing through."

"Who are you here to see —"

"Just passing through."

"Hi, this must be your first vis—"

"Just passing through."

I waited in the small sitting room outside his office, leafing through past issues of Psychology Today, National Geographic, and Vogue. I noticed plastic ferns sitting on the ledge of a partition wall across the room and wondered why people even bother to buy imitation plants, so obviously fake. The purpose of a plant is to give life to a room, create an environment more accommodating to us humans.

If you're going to buy imitation plants, why not just buy imitation books? Or plastic people. Better yet, real people who have died so that they are now stuffed with sawdust or some durable equivalent; lifeless, yet they live on forever in semi-suspended animation. We could collect them like trophies the way we do animals.

"Hey man, you know Elvis lives back at my house. I have his head stuffed and mounted on a board, hanging over the fireplace."

"Cool!"

Pretty sick thought. Anyway, I was having a really strange day. John was having one, too. He emerged from his office twenty minutes late, which I would later learn was common practice for him. Apparently the couple before me virtually decided during the course of their therapy session to file for divorce. A shouting match ensued, ugly words followed by cutting accusations.

John had brought the couple back from the brink of divorce. They would be returning the next day to continue the session. Before I entered, John walked around the room, chiming a set of Tibetan bells he used to relieve the room of unwanted negative energy. He then beckoned me into his office and introduced himself.

"Mark?"

"That's right."

"I'm John."

"It's nice to meet you, John."

"Why don't you take a seat?"

I sat down in a cushioned chair, facing John's desk piled high with papers, books and folders. His desk wasn't neat, but he seemed to be organized in such a way that everything was easily accessible. I was about to ask him why he had a series of broken tennis rackets tucked away in a corner against the wall, when he sat down across from me and began the session.

"So, tell me about yourself. I know a little bit about you from your father. I know you've been sick for a while, which is something you've struggled with. But, tell me more about you — where you're from, what your interests are, that sort of thing."

I briefly recounted the history of my illness, discussed my family, talked about my time at school and how it was I ended up in Toronto. Once we basically got acquainted, John had me play a little game. Holding out a deck of clear plastic cards with random pictures on them, much like Rorschach blots, he asked me to, "select from this series of cards the six you like most. When you've completed that, I want you to choose from this stack of colored cards, the six you like most and place them as background colors to the pictures you chose from the first deck."

"And what is this supposed to tell us?" I asked.

"When you've finished, I'll compare them against this chart and hopefully it will give us some indication of your psychological profile."

"I see." I was curious to hear what the cards would say and I've always liked games, so I played along. Some people are afraid to play these kinds of games, afraid of what they might find. Others don't believe in it at all. They say random selection/sampling suggests nothing. Yet, sometimes we find logic in places where none exists. Open a good book to some random page the next time you're troubled, read what's there, and see how it applies. You'll be surprised by what you find, surprised by the power of your mind to guide you through connections that otherwise weren't even there.

With this attitude, I approached the results of John's test, which reconfirmed much of what I already knew and believed about myself. On a wheel that represented opposing ideas, each of the cards I chose stood out on the extremes. According to the test, I was split, heading six different ways. Not schizophrenic, but scattered. A man who held opposing interests, perceptions, and world views.

Nothing wrong with it. How boring the people who fit into one definable category? A man who likes money, becomes a banker all his life; a woman, she likes chocolate, gives up teaching to become his wife. Would-be prophet on a street corner preaching Jesus to the masses; petty thief, he's so blind, steals a stereo to buy some glasses. Cafe junkie reading Tolstoy, talking politics in a rage, "Society's a rapist, but this latte's all the rave!"

I always kept a diverse set of interests, held a diverse set of ideas. Hung around with a diverse group of friends. The issues underpinning my life were diverse, and left me divided: my divided family; the fact that my family moved around a lot when I was young, state to state, town to town, street to street; always moving in one direction, but thinking in three. What was it about me?

adaptation as the key to survival
changing faces to be accepted
so many faces, which one is my own
forever moving, never home
safety in movement, carefree and having fun
or so it may appear — appearance is everything

change that follows change
nothing ever remains the same
where am I on this road that seems so long

"live for the moment," without living in the moment
a world filled with moments
not a moment to yourself

close friendships are dangerous
each friend a potential burden when thrust into the spotlight
and worse, to be abandoned by that one you deeply love
so at arms length, you keep your distance instead

when pinned down, you squirm and wonder
what can be done to recapture the life that kept you flying
a *chameleon* on the run.

I needed to learn more and made an appointment to return the following week.

Chapter 9

Towards the middle of summer, the heat sweltered. Scattered people ducked into air-conditioned doorways, drinking cold Pepsi from oversized cups; all of them tanned from getaway weekends to Miskoka, Niagara on the Lake, cottages up past Barry, where the woods meet the water along the beaches of Lake Ontario.

I had been journaling, drawing, and writing poems every day in the black-spined notebook my dad gave me — a place to explore my thoughts, my ideas about the books I read. The discoveries I made in my therapy with John Wendt quenched my thirst for knowledge and learning. I was studying myself, probing the recesses of my mind, the annals of my history like a research scientist on the verge of a significant discovery.

Yet I needed more. The fact I was learning about myself was something intangible, immeasurable. I needed something to show for my time — something concrete. The classic over-achiever, I needed something I could point to, put my finger on, pick up, dangle around and say, "Look here, the fruits of my labor!" Nothing too strenuous, mind you. I was looking for something simple and fun, yet satisfying.

I met my guitar teacher Ray through an ad stapled to a telephone pole on Yonge Street. My dad saw it on the way to work one day and tore away the paper tab with Ray's name and phone number on it.

Ray was a couple years older than I, a math major

forced to withdraw from the University of Toronto for financial reasons. His parents no longer willing or able to support him, Ray lived together with his girlfriend, a photography student, in a one bedroom apartment a few blocks up from where we lived on Lascalles.

In his heart, Ray was a political activist with a socialist agenda. He believed in the welfare state, socialized medicine, and watchdogging the overlords of industry, who might otherwise take advantage of the working class. Earned his money by teaching guitar, temping, and moon-lighting in a wedding band that performed party hits like *Twist and Shout, Stairway to Heaven, American Pie,* and *What I Like About You.*

Every Wednesday afternoon, Ray came over to teach guitar. We jammed for an hour and a half, then talked for a half hour more. Still didn't feel great, so I geared the entire day around my lesson. No walk. No excessive reading. I took it easy before he came, to prepare myself, and after he left, to recuperate.

When I told Ray about my illness, he almost couldn't believe I was sick. "You don't look sick. You don't act sick while I'm around." Which is what I liked about Ray. For two hours each week all we focused on was playing guitar, the music, and politics. Didn't think about the way I felt, or the way I felt about the way I was feeling. We were just a couple guys having a good time surviving in the world.

As summer turned into fall, I chose not to return to Berkeley. Wasn't yet up to starting school. I knew that if I did I would be right back where I started when I left — struggling to graduate, struggling to achieve a goal that was at that time unattainable as a result of my illness.

Didn't return to Los Angeles either. There was nothing there for me — nothing to be learned, nothing to be gained. I had visions of myself holed up in my mom's house, a veritable cage with invisible bars and no foresee-able way out.

At least in Toronto, the center of the city was just blocks from our apartment. I could walk out to Yonge Street and watch the people pass by. I could walk down to the corner and watch little kids playing frisbee in the park. I could feel as if I was part of civilization.

Besides, I had embarked on a spiritual journey into my subconscious, reading voraciously through books like John Lee's *The Flying Boy,* Robert Bly's *Iron John,* and Sam Keen's *Fire in the Belly.* These books talked about what it meant to be a male adult in today's society and the pressures/difficulties most men face.

For me manhood was a confusing concept — mixed messages and stereotypes, years of trying to prove my manhood by the beers I drank ... and the babes I bashed.

I remember being a pall bearer in a funeral for one of my best friends during high school. We were drinking one Saturday night, heavily; playing drinking games — like quarters, thumper, caps; cannonballing bong hits with shots of liquor and cans of Coors — or was it Bud?

Steve was going to drive another one of our friends home — Matt, who was so drunk he passed out at the table and started sliding off his chair onto the barf colored/covered shag carpet floor.

"Steve, are you sure you're okay to drive?" someone asked.

"Why don't you just let Matt crash on the couch?" another chimed in. "He can't face his parents like that anyway."

"Give me a break," Steve said. "I'm fine. And Matt told me earlier, he has to go home tonight."

"Are you sure, man?"

"Look, don't worry about it. I also want to pick up some smokes. I'll be back in twenty minutes."

"All right. Do you think you can pick up another twelve pack while you're out?"

"Sure," he said. At least he'd be picking up beers. So, we carried Matt — feet dragging, mouth drooling with really bad breath — out to the car and buckled him in. Engine and lights switched on, then they were gone.

Twenty minutes passed, then thirty; forty and we started worrying. After an hour passed, we went looking for him. We figured he had probably gone to Matt's, only to pass out there himself. But his car wasn't in the driveway.

We split up, taking different routes, hoping to find Steve driving the back streets or passed out on the side of the road — we were drunk ourselves, like wild ravens driving in the black night.

We caught site of him up Westridge Road, half a mile up the snake-back curves, overturned in his car. Lights flashed from an ambulance already on the scene. Matt was wearing his seatbelt and woke up hanging upside down, screaming. Steve wasn't wearing his seatbelt. When the car flipped, his head clipped the pavement, leaving him in a coma. He died five days later.

At the funeral, I remember one of my friends commenting on how strong I had been, that I hadn't been crying. Instead I just sat there solemnly as the preacher gave a very moving memorial service mixed with messages, laced with memories.

Looking back, I realize it had nothing to do with strength. I was simply too numb to cry. Not from the shock of Steve's death, but from years of being told to, "Act like a man. Be strong. Be a man." I was sad, yet unable to feel my sorrow. So, I prayed for Steve every night instead; prayed to God to give me some kind of sign that would let me know he was okay — just my little way of dealing with something I didn't want to deal with.

At this point in Toronto, I had learned enough to understand that not crying at one of your best friend's funeral isn't something about which you should be proud. It's something to be concerned about.

In today's society, men are supposed to be achievers. Striving for the top where the bottom line is the only thing that matters. At the same time, men are supposed to be compassionate, sensitive, caregivers and takers, family men, looking out for the little guy, concerned about the underclass, and whenever possible, politically correct.

We're supposed to accept the new role of women in the workplace, women as equals. Yet the chivalric code is still very much in vogue — opening doors, footing the bill for lunch, dinner, a movie. We're supposed to be able to laugh, cry, yet be strong at the same time.

Couldn't help wondering how any one man could maintain that facade of strength and confidence at the very same moment he was weeping with pain. The quest for power and money. Long hours away from home. Their souls sold so long ago, they don't realize the repercussions until it's too late and they've gone through a divorce, suffered a heart attack, reached fifty-five and realized they'd spent the last forty years of their lives working toward some slip-shod ideal passed down by society that says success equals happiness.

Success doesn't equal happiness. Happiness equals happiness, and happiness is only a small part of a larger idea called peacefulness. So, for these men, as they look back over their lives, not only do they wonder what went wrong, but to make matters worse, they ask the wrong question. When they ask, "Why am I not happy?" they should really be asking, "Why am I not at peace?"

The mid-life crisis ensues: stylish new suits with silk sweet ties; brand new sports car, preferably cherry red with a convertible top; casual glances at young women at opposite tables over dinner with their wives. They settle for their secretary, that sophisticated little blond who brings them coffee in the morning, "Is there anything else you need, Mr. So-and-so?"

Sure, I may be stereotyping the male mid-life crisis. But, in Toronto, I knew I was already enduring a major young adult life crisis. Didn't want to eventually experience a mid-life crisis, too. So I stayed with my dad to continue my inner work, probing the hidden membranes of my mind.

I took time to grieve the death of my friend Steve, the death of my grandfather, the breakup of my family. I started searching for answers to questions like: what does it mean to be a man in today's society? What does it mean to be an adult? At what moment does that occur? Is it something I am just going to feel or know? What is the appropriate way to express anger, use power, treat people, treat myself? What are my primary fears? What am I, who am I, when does it all become clear?

The more questions I asked, the more that came to mind. Talked to John about my questions, talked to my dad and Gordeen. I listened to tapes, read books. Like the temblor that causes a hairline crack to form on the outer wall of a large water dam, something gave way inside of me. I tapped into an aspect of myself, the depth of which I could not comprehend. It was only a matter of time until the dam broke and the walls came down. Knowledge that might lift me from my illness. Knowledge that could drag me further down.

*C*hapter 10

I was four years old when my parents completed their Harvard graduate degrees and moved west to southern California where I grew up. Wasn't until my junior year of college, that I returned to Harvard to witness the changing seasons, the falling leaves.

I flew back to visit my best friend from high school, something I talked about doing for a long time until I just decided to go for it. It rained a lot that year. But the week I arrived, the dark clouds had migrated up the coast and the sun shone down on Harvard Yard and the Charles River.

While my friend went to class, I took walks along the river bank. Watched rowers glide their skiffs, flawlessly stroking the water ... rambled through the fallen leaves ... breathed the crisp clean air and discovered for the first time that fall in the East was my favorite time of year.

Living in Toronto, I anxiously awaited the changing of the leaves. Leaves that, six months before sprang up vital and new, eventually grow tired. The withering summer heat rapidly aging youth and innocence, yields in nature's last gasps an immaculate death, beautiful and humbling, while winter waits in the wings to blanket the earth for a long deserved rest; a prolonged period of slumber, after which the cycle merely repeats itself the following year.

There exists this obvious cyclical theme in nature — the earth circles the sun once each year, the moon circles the earth once each month, the rise, fall and subsequent rise of the tides, the changing seasons, patterns that repeat themselves over and over again. Rise. Fall. Death. Rebirth. Take a look at women and the fertility cycle — the cycle that begins all human life. It peaks for a short period of time each month, to be followed by menstruation, the flushing of the uterus, only to repeat itself again.

Yet, we torment ourselves over the cycles in our own lives. When things are bad, we're depressed. When things are good, we're euphoric. We never anticipate the down-cycle of success, or the upcycle of failure. We cling to life, a precious commodity to be cherished — and it should be. But, to fear death as something terminal, everlasting, especially when we experience it through the seasons each passing year is ludicrous. Life gives way to death, just as death gives way to new life.

Drove out to witness death firsthand and up close — acres of trees in the meadows and the forests outlying the city. We had lunch in Kleinburg, a small town outside Toronto, famous for four Canadian painters who spent their summers painting countryscapes — streams, ponds, flowers, and trees displayed now in the McMichael Art Gallery and coveted throughout the land.

However, around this time, problems started brewing, like a kettle brought to boil, cold winds stewing. In my therapy, I began the slow slide into my dark side, the purgatory of my rage and grief. Tensions were building, too hard to ignore. A reality check was settling in. I was living in Toronto in a three-room apartment. Living room. Bathroom. Kitchen. And the walls were starting to close in on me. Either that, or the walls weren't thick enough.

The problem with two men living in a bachelor apartment is that when you need a little space, somewhere to hide your face for a few moments of privacy, you've got nowhere to go.

My dad found his privacy in the bathroom. Took the phone in there to talk with Gordeen. They talked every night, sometimes once, sometimes twice. When they argued he often hung up on her, or she on him. The phone would ring a couple minutes later and they would be at it again, sometimes an hour, many times all night.

Sitting in the other room, I could hear them, but not by choice. Even tried taking my guitar out on the balcony, strumming, singing loudly out into the night, street lights shining, but it didn't matter. My dad's voice would penetrate the closed bathroom door, reverberate across the living room, and through the glass balcony door to where I sat, trying not to listen.

I could hear him groveling, whimpering, tail between his legs, like a dog under the shadow of his master's broom.

"You're right, Gordeen ... I know, I'm sorry ... I should have been more understanding, more thoughtful ... Should have done this ... Next time I'll try to do that ... I'll do anything, just don't be mad at me. I just want you to love me. I'll do anything you ask ... I know, I'm sorry — you're right, Gordeen."

Round and round like a merry-go-round. Like the Allied Powers Policy of Appeasement towards Hitler during World War II, my dad gave ground, backed off, gave in, and folded at every turn, fueling Gordeen's rage still further. No one likes a worm.

He would walk out of the bathroom, face drawn and beaten. I could see the frustration in his eyes as he lumbered over to the couch and fell silent in front of the television.

Like anyone going through a difficult time, he talked to me about his problems. He talked to me often about the way nothing he tried, said, or did was ever good enough for Gordeen. He wondered what he could do. What he could say to get her back and make things better between them. So afraid of being abandoned by her altogether, he would sacrifice himself, his thoughts, his feelings, especially his pride, like a lamb led to slaughter.

Yet, my father was no lamb, no innocent. His motives were selfish, playing mind games and head games — anything for love. I hated seeing him that way, listening to the way he let her walk all over him. Always wanted my father to be strong and powerful, a man I could look up to and revere, emulate, respect. But how could I respect him, if he couldn't even respect himself?

"Why do you put up with that?" I would say, not even aware of the complexity of the situation. "Why do you let her march all over you, chew you up and spit you out, like a wad of gum?"

It made me mad so I tried to tell him what to do. Tried to tell him how to fight his battles, win his wars. The answers seemed so obvious to me, the truth so stunningly clear.

He listened, dangled his troubled marriage over the dining room table like an oversized worm from the barb of a worn steel hook, and I took the bait. I took on my father's problems and made them my own.

I'd say, "First, you've got to ... Then, you've got to ... Hang it up. Walk away, even for a short while. Take a break, until you find yourself, then come back on your own terms."

But he never did. He continued on in his ways, in his defeat, gaining ground through appeasement, then losing it in their next round of controversy.

Guess in a strange way, I was doing to my dad what Gordeen was doing to him — asking him to be something other than what he was, asking him to change. I demanded he be the type of man, the father, he had never been — the father I always wanted. In so doing, I found myself being sucked further and further into the middle of their tangled marriage.

Listening in on their telephone tantrums made me madder and madder — he, the spineless worm, she the tyrant. Had no idea what they were fighting about, or who was at fault. Yet, he, the spineless worm, she the tyrant.

I got so mad, I started wearing *his* shoes:

old man, how often have I worn your shoes
shoes that did not fit,
how often have I donned your armor
to wage the battles you would not wage,
how often have I screamed the words
you would not scream,
cried your tears, felt your pain

I've got a present for you, old man
Open it! Look inside!
That's right, they are your shoes
and I'm giving them back

I took up his side of the battle at every point that his defenses fell short of the mark. It got to the point, I was arguing with myself. Every time she called, every time he walked into the bathroom with the telephone clutched in his hands, my anger churned, the war raged in my head. In my mind, it was me in my dad's shoes taking on Gordeen, but I was really just arguing with myself.

Tension grew and grew and grew. For a while, I fought it, pretending nothing was wrong. But I was becoming an emotional time bomb. Tick. Tick. Tick. Just a matter of time until I went off.

Chapter 11

The other side to the equation driving my rage to the point of hysterical release — the point in which I was so fed up, pent up, shook down, ready to lose my mind — resulted from my relationship with Gordeen. While Gordeen and I generally had common interests and seemed to enjoy each other's company, an undercurrent of tension existed between us.

Perhaps Gordeen felt a little jealous of my relationship with my father. Perhaps I felt a little jealous of her relationship with my father. The things she saw him doing for me, were separate but parallel to the things I saw him doing for her. And I think both of us felt whatever my father was doing for us individually clearly fell short of the mark.

Still, the problem had more to do with our relationship with each other than with issues surrounding our relationship with my dad. Never quite felt comfortable around Gordeen. Always felt like I had to be on my toes, on my guard, ever conscious of a frontal assault on my person. We would sit around the dinner table discussing some issue:

"I went driving out to the country this weekend," I'd lead off. "It's so beautiful out there. With the downturn in the economy, it sure would be a great time to buy property."

"I wouldn't say that," she'd counter. "Prices are going to continue to fall. Why do you think so many developers are pulling out of their investments, taking losses and waiting for prices to fall farther so they can buy back in?"

Continuing my own line of reasoning, as I always

loved a good intellectual challenge, I'd respond: "Prices have fallen thirty percent. They've already taken the biggest hits. At this point, the best thing to do is ride it out."

This would lead her to invoke the bandwagon consensus argument, hoping I would jump right on. "All the economists I have read are saying we're experiencing a global contraction not seen since the Great Depression, which is just going to get worse. Are you telling me they're wrong?"

Gordeen is beginning to grow visibly angry, still hoping I might back down. The tension builds. Charlene sits across from me at the table in silence, watching the argument unfold.

"I don't know which economists you're reading for your information," I'd say, "but the ones I've read certainly wouldn't agree with that. Fact is, I am an economist. What do you think I've been studying at Berkeley for the past three-and-a-half years? And if you consider the rate at which the global population is growing, and the rate at which land is becoming more and more scarce, sure, we might be experiencing a temporary contraction, but in the long run land prices can only go up!"

At which point Gordeen would essentially snap, saying, "I don't really care about land scarcity, prices can just as easily go up as down etc. etc." Can't remember exactly how that argument ended. On the surface it seemed like a basic disagreement — two people with strong opinions debating a moderately interesting topic from subjective points of view.

And yet, the more time we spent together, the more frequent these disagreements became. I couldn't say whether she felt threatened by me in some way, or whether she felt threatened by everything and everyone around her and was just extremely sensitive. But it got to the point that every time we spent time something came up, and I was defending myself for something I said, or didn't say but Gordeen implied.

She would attack me. She'd be in my face, crowding my space, rage in her eyes, spewing out psychobabble: "You need to look at this. Need to take a look at that. If

87

you're going to get better, you need to address your anger towards women."

She moved so quickly from calm to anger, sometimes I wondered whether or not I should take her seriously and even address her anger. I could at times diffuse her, if I could pinpoint the issue that set her off. But most of the time, her anger just made me angry.

At first, it didn't. I just blew it off. But the more time I spent with her, the deeper I became embroiled in the relationship between her and my father, and the more she got under my skin.

I saw parallels between my relationship with Gordeen and my dad's relationship with her. She was a control freak and used her anger to control others: she always had to be right, always had to have things her way. If you let her, she kept you tiptoeing around her sensitivities, until you were constantly afraid to ignite her anger, infuse her rage.

I remember having lunch one time with Gordeen and my dad. Gordeen was talking about Charlene, who had gone off to college, and who would call up crying on the phone, sobbing because she was so homesick up at school. Gordeen made some comment that she was trying to wean Charlene out of the nest — slowly. Apparently, weaning Charlene was difficult for her to do, when her motherly instinct wanted to tell her to come straight home.

"Yeah," I said, trying to relate to her. "Sometimes you just have to give them a little nudge, that's all. Help 'em along."

Immediately she pounced on me. "You're not exactly out of the nest yourself you know. You're still living at home. You have no right to be so pompous!"

I glanced across the table, hoping to get some support from my dad, only to realize I was looking in the wrong place. I could see the fear in his eyes, trembling in the face of her anger.

"I'm not being pompous," I replied. "I think you're a little sensitive about this. And maybe I wasn't recognizing that completely, but I don't think it has anything to do with my being pompous."

Here I managed to concede a little, without folding and

saying, "You're right. You're completely right. I'm sorry I offended you."

Because she wasn't right. She made an issue of something that really shouldn't have been one. At least as far as I could tell. I congratulated myself later for my brinkmanship, yet at the same time I burned with anger — burned over Gordeen's assault on me, and over my dad's recoil from her anger.

I needed my dad for support, yet I watched him crumble each time Gordeen became angry. Each time Gordeen exploded, I put on my father's shoes, my mind screaming, "you can't control me!" Because if my dad, the man who raised me, couldn't stand up to her power, where did that leave me? Therefore, not only did I have to prove that I wasn't afraid of her, I had to make it so my dad was not afraid of her either, because the moment my dad stood up for himself, he would become the father I always wanted and I would get the love I always needed but never got. Notice the complexity of this crazy loop?

Each time Gordeen and I got together, she was in my face, breaching my space, insinuating male chauvinism, my pompous inflexibility — both of which were entirely insane. Yet, she hammered away at me, so that I began to doubt even myself. Sick. Tired. I was insecure as a result of my illness, and of my status/non-status in the world.

In my face so fast, plus I was already bringing anger to the table. "You can't control me. You may be able to control my dad, but you can't control me!" was the mantra repeated over and over in my head. I was just looking for the right opportunity to prove it to her; show my dad how it was done — how to control his woman, or at least keep his woman/women from controlling him. Women had always controlled him. Probably had something to do with his mother, some kind of mommy complex. Just wanted to be loved, anything, everything for love.

Yet I was trying to maintain my bond with Gordeen because I cared about her. She was definitely a little intense for me, but I respected her. I appreciated the things she did for me, and the way she cared for me. I appreciated the way she encouraged me in my learning, and on my path. Always offering me a new book, or presenting me with something to think about — a new challenge.

So, every time we got together, she was in my face in that way in which you knew she was just about to lose it. I couldn't understand why, because her anger was out of proportion with the limits of reason. Yet, I couldn't do anything to defend myself, because I had far too much anger of my own I was trying to control. Kept telling my therapist, "if I let go (cause she's right there, too), we're going all the way to hysteria and I don't want to go that far, risk our friendship." I knew I couldn't contain my anger, which bubbled and brewed.

She continued to assault me, lashing me with the whip of her tongue, serving up poisoned apostrophes. Each time I held back my anger, eating it as it brewed, bubbled, and grew, until I just couldn't hold on any longer — couldn't go on any longer.

It happened on a Wednesday. I made plans with Gordeen to go to the movies a few days before and told her I would call to confirm our plans. Didn't know how I would be feeling that day, or whether or not I would be up to it.

I held off calling her till the last moment — a few hours before we were scheduled to meet. When I did call, she said she was busy. Said she'd already made plans for that evening. Said I should have called sooner.

And she was right. Still, I decided this was my night to stand up for myself, express my disappointment in a mature manner. She could have at least called to tell me she was making other plans, I reasoned. So I picked up the phone and called her back.

"Hello."

"Gordeen, this is Mark. Listen, I just wanted to tell you that I was really disappointed when you told me you made other plans and I think you should have at least called me."

"What do you mean, *I* should have called?" she retorted, as she started to lay into me. "You shouldn't have waited until the last minute to call me. You didn't call, so I made other plans."

"Look, you're way out of line!" I rumbled, but before I could continue, she hung up on me. When she did, oddly enough I felt a little freer, a little more alive, as if a door held shut had flown open, clearing all passages to the center of my being. She spoke to the beast within me and my beast within spoke back. I reveled in the thought of that.

Five minutes later, she called. You can see how sick the patterns, how thick the cross-over and confusion woven through our lives. It was the same routine she developed with my father, and it was now being played out with me. In that instant, I became him. This was my chance to show him, as he stood listening in the next room — show him, show her, she could not control me.

A few words of 'I'm sorry' passed between us. At first we were making amends, saying we both went slightly overboard. Yet, I needed to go farther. Couldn't stop there. Had to clear my conscience completely. Now that we were apologizing, revealing ourselves, I felt the need to reveal my pain and divulge the torment I was going through each time we got together. I started in, but she didn't want to listen. I was nervous, not expressing myself effectively. After all she had been through with my father, she didn't want to go through it with me. Her anger erupted once again; she attacked me and I lost it — we both did.

She screamed. I was delirious with rage, no control over what I was saying. I was a different person, someone I had never met before, a crazy, a lune. When she threatened:

"I'm going to hang up!"

I said, "Go ahead!"

"If I do, you'll never talk to me again!"

"Then do it!"

"I'm going to hang up!"

"Do it!"

"I swear I'll hang up!"

"DO IT!!"

She slammed the receiver down. I was shaking from head to toe. So weak, I had to sit, breathe deeply, calm down. My dad walked over, sat down, and held me as I trembled in his arms.

When the room stopped floating and I recovered, I felt

91

purged, like a vicious demon had been exorcised from my being.

I wasn't sure if I would ever talk to Gordeen again. At that point, I didn't care. Didn't really want to think about it either. I was tired. Pulled my mattress from the fold-away couch and covered it with sheets, blankets, my pillow. Laid down, closed my eyes, and went to sleep. Didn't even brush my teeth.

Chapter 12

Sometimes I find myself open to the beauty in life, the magic that tingles in the air all around me. I feel alive with the sun on my face, the wind at my back; I raise my arms and let the warm Santa Ana winds lift me into the air, until I'm dancing on cloud nine.

But soon my perspective shifts. I realize I'm twenty thousand miles above the earth's surface slipping through the troposphere at an average speed of 9.8 meters per second without a parachute. I'm in free fall, frozen wind burning my face. Some joker on the ground's gonna break my fall with a thimbleful of water spread evenly over a quarter mile of hard-packed dirt.

Just as I'm about to go splat, the sky above softens. I'm taking the Nestea plunge off the bow of a forty-foot schooner into the crystal blue Caribbean.

My dad and I moved in mid-November to an apartment on Jackes Avenue with more room than our previous place. Three bedrooms. Two baths. The kitchen was twice the size of the last one.

The apartment was nicer, too. Wood floors. A doorman to let you in. We had a bird's-eye view of the city — our living room was one long stretch of sliding glass. At night the city lights trembled and glittered off the skyscrapers in downtown Toronto, the kind of view you might find on a postcard.

We were so high up that when I walked out onto the

93

balcony my balls tingled, my stomach fluttered. Peering over the edge, the first thing I thought was, "Wonder what would happen if I jumped?" My balls would tingle a little more, so I'd step back from the rail, afraid I might bungle-trip-stumble and go plunging head first, arms flailing, to a terrible death below.

Autumn reached its tumultuous end. The last of the golden leaves fluttered to the ground. I was steadily extending my trip. I originally planned to stay only a month. One month became two. Decided to stick it out for the entire summer, only to extend my trip again to remain for the fall. I was on a temporary stay that was becoming more and more permanent.

But at the same time, it could never be permanent. I never considered Toronto my home. I was a visitor, an outsider, a Los Angelean. I liked it that way; liked the fact I had a place to run back to, run away to. If things weren't working out for me in Toronto, I could always return to Los Angeles. Remember, I was a chameleon and didn't want to feel pinned down to any one place, state, country.

In many ways my outsider status made me feel special, different, a stranger in a strange land. Everybody likes a stranger, likes the danger of someone foreign, someone different from themselves — with different experiences, a different take on life.

"Oh, you're from California," they'd say and smile knowingly — grin, nudge, grin. "What are you doing here? It's so cold. Ever see any movie stars? Everyone's so shallow out there. And how about those beaches. I have some friends who live in San Mateo."

"That's in northern California. I live in southern California."

"That's right. I've been thinking about driving out to visit them. Think I should?"

What do I look like, a fucking travel agent? "Sure, I think it'd be a great idea."

It shouldn't have surprised my mom when I decided to stay the winter, but it did. She wondered why I was staying. She missed me. She worried about me.

"It's going to get really cold."

"I know."

"The winters are long and dark. What happens if you get worse?"

"I won't."

"But, what if you do? Wouldn't you be better off coming back to Los Angeles where at least it doesn't snow?"

"There's nothing there for me right now. I've got nothing to go back to. I've got to stay here. I really can't explain it, it's just something I have to do."

Been a long time since I experienced winter — a real winter anyway. Growing up in California, it rained sometimes. It even got cold during the winter, or at least "chilly." It never snowed.

My only memories of snow growing up came from ski trips — Ski & Pack tours to Utah and Mammoth, day trips to Big Bear, and the one time I went to Aspen with the family of my best friend from junior high.

I used to tell my parents I had memories of the year we lived in Point Barrow, Alaska. My dad was on assignment there as part of his six-year tour in the Naval Engineering Corps. Memories of a day when I stood with my dad on the bow of a ship frozen in the ice, frozen until the following summer, when the warm weather would set the ship free once more.

Yet, I was only three years old when we lived in Alaska. My most lucid memory was a picture pasted in the back of an old family album.

I was looking forward to the snow; looking forward to walking in winter. Frozen lakes. Frozen ponds. Snow angels. Snowball fights. The delicate white flakes melting on my tongue. Boyhood dreams — a winterland of ice and wonder.

The main reason I stayed the winter in Toronto was that the parameters which led me to Toronto in the first place remained unchanged: my illness; my need to "find" my father; the feeling of stagnation I felt in Los Angeles/Berkeley; and the opportunity for personal/spiritual growth I experienced in Toronto.

Truth was, I felt I was actually onto something. The road less traveled (avoided by most altogether and at all costs). While I knew I would at some point return to California to resolve some issues there, I also had several unresolved issues still in Toronto. My mission was not yet complete.

My health certainly hadn't improved since I arrived — up a couple weeks, down the next. Each month that passed made it more and more difficult to remember what it was even like to be healthy. I was so far removed from my life as a student, an athlete, a fraternity guy, that life in the workforce seemed unfathomable.

Perhaps I should have taken this as a sign that my stay in Toronto wasn't working out, but I was still hopeful at this point that things would turn around, that I would soon start feeling better. If I left before I was ready, questions would linger. If I flew to Los Angeles unhealthy, unhappy, and remained so after I arrived, I would always question my decision to come back. I had to stay.

Gordeen was still in the picture. My dad saw her occasionally, talked to her on the telephone, albeit less frequently. He was still trying to salvage their marriage, forge through lull, tide, convergence, divide.

Gordeen and I tried to patch our friendship back together, as well. We talked on the phone from time-to-time, sharing ideas, insights, but the trust was gone. The issues surrounding our argument lingered. I held back, delicately traversing my path over slippery stones slightly deeper than shallow, extending my heart one moment, withdrawing it the next. So did she.

Within a couple months our relationship crumbled altogether. All contact ceased. Wrote her a letter telling her why, a letter delivered by my father. Wanted her to know how the confusion set in motion from the onset of our relationship was more than I could manage: I harbored too much anger toward my father directed onto her; toward her, directed onto me. I couldn't seem to sort it all out.

Felt it was better to simply write her goodbye, then get away, and get clear.

She tore it up. Guess I should have expected it. When I told my father of my intention, he became part of the loop. Letters were always a form of venting for my father. He'd start off nice and sweet: *Don't want to upset you, but I thought you should know how I feel* ... then go into some obscene tirade.

These were the type of letters Gordeen came to expect from him. I imagine when he delivered my letter, she expected the same from me — a sugar-coated stink bomb in a folded paper jacket.

She said if I had something to say, I should say it directly to her. But I had nothing to say, nothing to talk about. I just wanted to get away, go my own way. In my heart it felt better to let her know why she'd been betrayed.

Sad thing about betrayal is the people we hurt, when we prevent them from hurting us. Robert Bly says there exists a natural brutality in nature and that betrayal is part of that. And he's right.

Someone is attacking you, bullying you, trying to run your life. For a while, you let them. Then the day comes you don't let them anymore, and that becomes a betrayal. You're merely standing up for yourself, but you've betrayed the other person. You've taken from them the fulfillment, or whatever you want to call the satisfaction they get out of bullying you.

Sad thing about betrayal is the loss we endure when at last we decide to betray. We let that same person bully us, because by letting that person bully us, we get something we want. At least we think we do: we think we get love, friendship, respect; we think we get to be part of the crowd.

So when we betray, we lose something. I know I did. In an effort to gain my sanity, I lost a friend. Actually, I lost two. When I chose to cut Gordeen out of my life, I knew Charlene would never understand. Knew they were too close, that to lose one meant to lose both, and I was right. But I made my choice consciously, the consequences weighed considerably in my mind, until the choice became something I could live with; a trade-off along the road to spiritual clarity; the first in a series of steps I would take to cleanse my soul, to get to the bottom of all I was told, and make sense of a world that did not make sense to me any more.

Winter rapidly approached, and I experienced the first of many snow flurries. I was excited over the new possibilities that awaited me in my new apartment — my own bed, my own room, a tree-lined ravine a short walk from the front door of our building. My guitar playing had steadily improved. My therapy progressed. My relationship with my father had grown to a level of comfort and trust unparalleled since the early years of my childhood.

I visited yet another doctor, another attempt to rid myself of illness. She was a very attractive young Indian woman, fresh out of medschool, and part of a small innovative health clinic, specializing in the treatment of *candida albicans.*

Candida is a yeast/fungus which lives and grows naturally in our intestines. For most it is harmless. Yet, when the body is rundown, exhausted, and burdened by long-term illness or disability, candida overgrowth can occur, causing toxicity which further burdens the immune system. Then you're not only fighting the virus that made you sick in the first place, but the toxicity from the yeast infection as well. Still largely overlooked, if not shunned, ignored, and dismissed by much of the medical community, candida can potentially cause skin rashes, allergies, fatigue, and nausea.

The doctor running the clinic left on sabbatical and obviously was not seeing new patients, which was how I met Tina, my doctor. She shook my hand harder than most men the day we met; she wanted to let people know she was a professional.

"Mark, I received the tests back on your yeast count. It's incredibly high."

"Really."

"I can't say for sure if it's the underlying reason you feel the way do. However, I do believe it's playing a significant role in the level of fatigue you're experiencing."

"Comparatively speaking, how high is it? And once it's treated how much better can I expect to feel?"

"Well, to be honest with you. I've seen a lot of patients much worse off than you, with yeast counts lower than yours, that once treated through medication and diet, returned essentially to full health within a few months."

"That's incredible. So, there's a chance I could be completely better in a few months."

"That's right. We'll be starting you off on Niastatin, which is something we commonly use to treat candida."

"Okay. You know my body is really sensitive to medication. Are there any side-effects?"

"You could feel a little worse at first, as the fungus dies off and is eliminated from your body. So for you, you might want to start off by taking half a dose. Then slowly work your way up to one full tablet three times a day. Most likely, you won't experience any side-effects at all. Come back and see me in a month."

"All right. Thanks. I'll see you in a month."

Still, I was a little skeptical. I frequently reacted to medications and even vitamins doctors recommended I take, but I felt compelled to try it. Here for the first time was some tangible evidence for my malaise. In all the tests I took, nothing ever showed. Test results up to this point had been negative. This was something physically wrong — and it was treatable!

"This could be it," I told my dad, as I stepped into the car. "She says I've got candida. One of the worse cases she's seen (always loved to embellish). Said, if things go well, I could be healthy in a couple months."

I brought the medication home, held it firmly in my hand, admiring it as if it were magic — an elixir of the gods passed down to offer me a miracle cure. Popped open the top. Took one pill — envisioned myself running again; then two — saw myself laughing, out to dinner with friends. Four hours later, I took two more.

She said I should start to notice something within the first week — more energy, a lighter step, mental clarity. It would be slow and subtle at first, but increase as the weeks passed, with total relief just a few months away.

99

After three weeks I didn't notice anything different — not the slightest fraction of improvement, one-to-the-one millionth — nothing. I went back to the doctor to ask why it wasn't working.

"For some, it takes a little longer than others, longer for the yeast to die off. Just be patient and keep taking it. You'll get better. You know, it's time you moved on with your life."

"You're right," I said. What else could I say? "Guess I'll just keep taking it. It's certainly not making me feel worse." I should have knocked on wood when I said that, or pounded the floor, or banged my head against a large oak door ...

"By the way, have you had your flu shot yet?"

"Flu shot?" I inquired.

"So you don't get the flu this winter. There's a really bad Indonesian strain going around this year. Better to be safe than sorry."

"Oh, I've never had one before."

"You should, it's a good idea. Why don't you see the nurse on your way out."

"All right."

I was from California. No one gets flu shots in California. I just figured this was one of those cold weather things, something everybody did. I sure as hell didn't want to contract some rare Indonesian flu, end up parched, perched in a cold sweat, shivering with delirium.

Besides, she was a doctor. She was my doctor, trying to protect me, cure me, relieve me of illness. She knew what she was doing, after all those years in medical school.

The nurse said I might experience some slight flu-like symptoms, but they would go away in a couple days. Another warning, but did I take it?

Lying on the cold vinyl table, pants down to my knees, I jerked as she stuck me with the long sharp needle.

The next day, I didn't have flu-like symptoms. There was nothing flu-"like" about it. I had the flu — sore throat, fever, chills — the whole tomato!

Had I not been given the shot, my chances of not getting the flu were seventy/thirty in my favor, maybe better.

In fact, while I suffered from fatigue, I rarely caught colds, the flu, or even got sick with other airborne illnesses — I had spent so much time inside and away from people.

Instead, I seemed to have cornered the market on obscure, semi-phantom, doctor-induced sicknesses: nausea that lasted for months; a parched throat that no matter how much I drank wouldn't go away. And now this "sort of" the flu. 'Cause it wasn't really the flu — just a slight fever, "sort of" the chills, "sort of" a runny nose.

I told the doctor she gave me the flu.

"That's impossible," she said.

"So is being fatigued for two years," I said.

Over the next few months she tried to cure my flu. B-12 shots. Gamma Globulin boosters. Nothing helped. Now I had chronic fatigue, coupled with chronic flu. Man, was I blue.

Sometimes I wonder if I stayed away from doctors altogether, whether I would have gotten my health back a lot sooner. Seemed like every doctor I went to was a quack.

That's because most doctors *are* quacks if you really think about it. More than a hundred years or so ago, doctors prescribed bleeding as a formal cure. If you had a serious case of scarlet fever, "doctors" would cut a series of incisions and let the "bad" blood flow out, or maybe cover you with leeches to suck the blood and purge the illness from your body. Wonder what the doctors will be saying a hundred years from now about all the slicing, dicing, testing, and treating that goes on today.

Truth is, the more doctors learn, the more they realize how little they know about the human body and the universe and sub-universe that comprise its essence. Even after you've identified and documented every little cell, every last molecule, every strand of DNA (which you know could never happen anyway with all the mutations and migrations and second/third generations), it all spirals back to the basic questions that can never be answered from our limited perspective: how did we get here? How do you take a molten planet, swirl the elements, cool it off and end up with this phenomenon life? How is it that fifteen billion years ago a glitch suddenly appeared in a void that didn't exist and instantly exploded to become our universe?

So you see, this quackery must continue. Most of the time (if not every time) a doctor gives you medicine, they couldn't tell you how it works to "cure" your illness. All they know is that it seems to work in most cases, or that it sometimes works, or merely that the pharmaceutical sales person that came by their office claimed it works better than the last barbiturate, antibiotic, pain killer he/she'd been peddling.

Most doctors still have very little understanding of basic nutrition. As a vegan, I had one doctor tell me I absolutely had to eat meat to get iron, and consume dairy products for calcium.

"It's good for your bones," he said.

Dairy products are the worst form of food on the planet. In fact, they shouldn't be considered food at all, and nutritionally should fall somewhere between Ding-Dongs and cow-pie. Tainted with steroids and antibiotics, most adults are incapable of digesting them properly — they don't have the enzymes in their stomach necessary to break them down. Why else would *lactaid* be a million dollar industry?

Growing up, I used to think milk cows just naturally produced milk year round. Wasn't until a couple years ago I learned that the reason cows produce milk is the same reason human mothers produce milk — to feed their young. They're impregnated, only to have their calves aborted, a cycle that happens a few times each year. Didn't surprise me to find out the average life span of a milking cow is two-and-a-half years. Wonder what the *Right to Lifers* would say? Wonder if each time they drink milk with their chocolate chip cookies they say a prayer for the unborn calf that gave them that glass of milk?

But, there I go again. Off on tangents. Always losing myself in tangents. Like a little mouse lost in a weblike maze, wandering down divergent paths, searching for a fat chunk, hankering for slab-slunk of milky white ... cheese.

*C*hapter 13

I walk this street, this thoroughfare
and breathe the pungent contempt for life
reverberating through the tendrils of the city.

I hear the screams, the latent cries
of people dying from the inside out.
I feel the onerous vibrations
of angry thoughts through lonely hearts
empty for love they will never acknowledge,
in environs so excruciatingly unjust
until selves that were no longer exist
and all they know is silence ...

How many wars have I waged
finally to concede
this world is not a battleground.

I had slipped to the bottom of an impossible emptiness,
a lion's den, a psycho-spiritual Hades. My days were
frozen, grey and cold. Outside the sun did not shine for
weeks on end.

Sick in my bed, it was difficult for me to walk around
the apartment; difficult for me to walk down the corridor to
the elevator six doors away.

I began each day with a sun stretch — a grouping of
yoga stretches designed to invigorate the body, which
served as my only form of exercise. My daily walk was

reduced to a trip down to the lobby, where I would sit for fifteen minutes and chat with the security guard — my only escape from our apartment that went from being a sanctuary to a twisted take on Rapunzel's tower. Twenty-six floors straight up. Some days even the lobby seemed far, too far down ... a distant oasis my weakened body could not reach.

I was down to a hundred and twenty-two pounds, emaciated to the point that by early January, my father asked, "Are you going to die?"

"No, I'm not going to die," I replied. "What kind of question is that? You're supposed to support me, console me, tell me things are going to be okay, not the other way around." Made me want to scream, so I did.

In the afternoons, I often took a bath and imagined myself engulfed in healing water, surrounded by golden candle flames filling me with light as their shadows danced on the bathroom walls to music by Pachelbel; the sound of waves crashing, nature's source surging through my body.

After my bath, I would nap. I liked listening to Meryl Streep tell the story of the Velveteen Rabbit, with George Winston playing piano in the background. Like the Velveteen Rabbit who, in the story, finds himself cast aside — "a mass of scarlet fever" to be burned with the rest of the garbage out behind the tool shed — I, too, felt cast aside.

When it came to the part in the story where the Velveteen Rabbit sheds a tear — a real tear — and a magical flower grows from where the tear has fallen, I would sometimes cry and imagine that my tears would one day bring forth the Nursery Magic Fairy, who would then carry me away and make my life real, just as she made the Velveteen Rabbit real.

Then, just before dinner, I would sit in the corner of my room and meditate in the lotus position. I'd stare into a long mirror I placed opposite myself; stare into my own eyes, and tell myself as if chanting a mantra: "I'm going to get better. I'm going to get better. You're going to be okay. Don't give up. I'mgoingtogetbetter. I'mgoingtogetbetter. You'regoingtobeokay. Don't-giveup."

And I never did give up. Never thought about suicide.

I was angry, afraid, frustrated. I could barely imagine what it would be like to be healthy, or how I could possibly get there. Each passing day my muscles atrophied further, and my mountain to climb grew more and more daunting. But I never gave up.

At the same time my health deteriorated, I delved deeper and deeper into my subconscious. I traced the pathways back to the core of my being, reliving the events and emotions that shaped my life, shaped who I was at that moment in time.

For me, the way back was through my pain, rage, hurt, which is why I embraced my suffering. I believed that the only way to heal myself, physically, spiritually, emotionally, was to go to the bottom — to the point I could not take it any more. Once there, maybe I would understand my pain, forgive those who hurt me most, and forgive myself for suffering under the burden of that pain for so long.

I focused on my parents, to know them as they really were; the way they treated me, loved me; the way they let me down.

I always knew my dad was a dog, because my mom perpetually reminded me of it growing up ... the way he left our family for another woman. Had always known my father was never around, too. He worked all the time, worked himself into the ground. That was why I came to Toronto, to rekindle the memories of the good times we shared and left behind.

My mom was different; she was always there for me. Could never say anything bad about her. She raised me, took care of me. Always counted on her growing up to pick me up from school, keep me fed, clothed, make sure I had everything I needed. She was mommy and I was her baby, until the morning I wrote a poem, which I appropriately titled — "Little Darling."

little darling, she called me
little darling conspiracy is what I recall
conspiracy against my father
an unspoken subterfuge of anger
the result of a marriage in shambles.

the only child of the unconscious seductress
she chose me —
her champion, her savior, her magnificent prince,
chose me to a task I so deeply desired
all at once my infantile fantasies fulfilled —
my mother mine, now my father killed.

tangled in this web that promised
falsely my deliverance in life,
I, the man-child, now hear the muted call
like that of some fog-engulfed ship
lost somewhere on a turbulent night's sea
of my stranded mother, as she hushedly beckons:
"Little Darling ... Little Darling ..."

like a sleepwalker following the querulous whispers
of a distant unconscious, or worse
the acquiescent caught in a vampirelike trance
I must cospond: "Yes Mommy ... Yes!"

As I wrote the poem, the catharsis I experienced was
extraordinary. Felt like I had given birth. Not that I would
know what it's like to give birth. But, from my perspective,
that's what I felt.

It's not that my mom and I shared a twisted relationship,
or that she took advantage of me, but it's no coincidence
the story of Oedipus has held up against time and remains
a classic today. It's no coincidence that Freud based much
of his research into the subconscious on the Oedipus complex.

My mom and I had what I would call a "special"
relationship. While I was growing up, she dumped her
pain surrounding her divorce with my father on me and I
took it, carried it, nurtured it. By age ten, I deemed myself
her savior in return for the way she took care of me.

Yet, this was only part of the problem. At an early age,
it became clear that I had won the battle for my mother's
affection, displaced my father as the apple of her attention.
He was at work, spent time away, and was distant when he
came home. She was alone. I was her child who needed
her, loved her, depended entirely upon her.

This special relationship with my mother affected my

relationship with other women — friends, girlfriends. I was that disconcerting combination of nice and indifferent. Let them walk on me, the way women walked on my dad, yet I'd play my little games, unwilling to commit; unwilling to let myself get too close, else they might feel they own me. Or worse still, I would find myself smothered by a relationship I couldn't control. One minute I felt my power usurped — giving it away. The next minute, I withdrew my love altogether, trying to prove I didn't care, didn't need them, couldn't be hurt, couldn't be controlled, couldn't feel *abandoned*.

I didn't talk to my mom for three months. I needed separation, perspective, space. I was angry, felt I'd been unconsciously dumped on and betrayed. When I told my mom I wasn't talking to her, she in turn felt dumped on and betrayed, as if I was losing my marbles, just like my father before me. "What is it about Canada that drives men to the brink of insanity?" she asked me the night I decided to stop talking to her.

"If anything, I'm trying to regain my sanity, and I just need some time to do that," I replied, which she couldn't understand. Yet, one thing was clear, I was mommy's *little darling* no longer.

Distancing myself from my mom enabled me to reevaluate my relationship with my father beyond the burden of his leaving our family; beyond the pleasure I experienced spending time with him. It enabled me to search my feelings toward him. What did I really think of this man? How did I feel about the way he treated me growing up? What was his role in my development? Which of his influences do I want to keep, which do I wish I could discard?

Reading this you might think, "This guy had far too much time on his hands." It's true, I did. Spent my days alone in a three-room apartment, when there was nothing but clouds outside.

But, these were things I had to know; questions that burned inside me for years. I'm clearly not my mom or dad. Who am I? We follow the ideas and guidance of our parents, because we need them, and get love from them. They take care of us and teach us how to take care of

107

ourselves. Without them, we'd be alone.

Trace every fear you've ever known and they all lead back to the one great fear — abandonment. The fear you will be left alone, all by yourself, no one to love. Starvation. Annihilation. Death. This fear starts in the crib, and for most, stays with us throughout our lives.

Sitting on my Japanese-style comforter, I came to this realization one day; nothing phenomenal, nothing I'm sure others haven't come to themselves, but for me served as the epiphany that unlocked the door to my heart.

I had built up so many walls: walls of anger towards my mom, dad, friends, and loved ones; walls of indifference; walls that left me numb; walls to keep me from feeling, when the pain was too much.

My dad and I spent a long time talking that night about my illness and the opportunity it gave me to understand my childhood. In Toronto, I was dependent upon him to take care of me; dependent upon him for social interaction; dependent upon him to help me around the city. In many ways, he was my only connection to the outside world, except for the occasional visit from my guitar teacher and the occasional dinner with my stepbrother and his girlfriend.

Focusing on our relationship, I was able to identify the messages I received from him growing up; mixed messages that were part love, coupled with his inability to express love; part indifference, wrapped up in his own life and world; part inspiration, his efforts to shape my young mind; part frustration and anger, the latent messages that at times I was a burden to him — needed too much, cost too much, kept him tied down like a tomcat on a leash.

My dad loved me, but he was not a caregiver. Yet, I wanted him to take care of me, to be there for me. Wanted him to be someone I could count on in every situation and at every turn.

In most situations, I could. But living with him day in day out was gradually becoming impossible. I was incapable of separating the love from the neglect. Knew at some point soon I would need to leave Toronto and return home to Los Angeles.

$\mathscr{C}$hapter 14

Spring was like nothing I'd experienced before; helped me to understand how the season got its name. After wandering through the quagmire of winter — six months in a slump, like a beast covered with mud, slugs, and other decaying debris — I felt like I had taken a long hot bath, with bubbles! Winter's blanket of death melted and gone.

In the first week of May, warm breezes blew through the city. The trees budded with lime green leaves. Small plants pierced up through the brown rich soil, fighting for the sky.

By the third week, life literally exploded. Red tulips in bloom on walkways that led to the park. Green grass — thick, cool, soft. Birds singing, crickets chirping, people playing frisbee in the park, relaxing in the sun, or under the branches of a large shade tree. All served up as inspiration, like a ceremony of miracles; spring gave me new life.

I started taking walks in the park. My dad and I would be moving again. He was renovating a house on Aldwych Avenue, east of the Don Valley Parkway.

During my visit, my dad began rebuilding his finances. He still didn't have money to burn, but the house he bought was a nice place. Three stories with a large finished basement. Converted by the previous owners into a three-unit apartment building, my dad was restoring it back to a single-family residence, knocking down walls, and putting in wood floors and skylights.

We moved in while the place was still being renovated, because renovations always take a little bit longer than everyone expects them to take. Things come up — wires and beams, uneven seams — unexpected things.

Spent my afternoons hanging out at the house: hammer-hammer-nail-saw-nail-saw-hammer. I hung with the building crew, ate lunch with them on their break. Wasn't doing any work on the place; I didn't have energy for that. I just hung, read books, and hung some more: hammer-hammer-nail-saw-nail-saw-hammer.

One of the guys was Jamaican. He liked to tell stories.

"You call that a mango?" he said to me one day.

"Yeah, what would you call it?" I said.

"Back home we have mangoes like this," and he held up his hands to demonstrate the size equivalent to a large honeydew melon.

"Really?"

"Oh yeah. We have papayas, minimum two feet long. And avocados," he added, shaking his head and smiling, "about the size of a Nerf football. Ever played with a Nerf football?"

"Of course."

"Well, then you know what I'm talking about."

When I told him I was vegetarian, he told me about a Caribbean stew called Callalou.

"First, you sauté the okra with onions; then add spinach, carrots and a mixture of other vegetables; throw in some Caribbean spices. You must try it."

"Where do you get the Caribbean spices?"

"There's a store nearby, where I live. I'll bring some one of these days and we'll make Callalou together." Of course, he never did, and I still haven't had Callalou. I've got the recipe though, and some day I'll make it.

The neighborhood felt comfortable, intimate. All the backyards, connected. Kids played in the streets, like the way I imagine Brooklyn was in the 1940s. Though honestly, I don't know what the 40s were like, and I've never been to Brooklyn.

My room was on the third floor. An attic that was now a two-bedroom loft. Small windows overlooked the back porch, which was lined with long boxes of potted flowers. Wasn't large, but it was comfortable, like a den or small cave with windows, pillows, and a thick blue carpet.

While it was technically my room, I knew I wouldn't be staying long. I was a guest, my visit temporary. I had lived in Toronto a year, stuck it out as my state of mental/physical health bottomed out through the long dark winter.

As I started to improve, I knew that Toronto was not the place for me. My dad was starting another relationship. I had school to finish and wasn't moving closer to that goal by living in Canada. Most of my friends lived back in California. I felt I reached the end of my learning curve.

I stopped seeing my therapist in April. During the winter months, I kept my appointments through phone visits, because I wasn't strong enough to visit him in person. I consulted with him an hour each week — my beacon through the fog, a series of signposts on the hard journey deep into my subconscious.

When I finally stopped seeing him in April, my solitude was so severe, my analysis so intense, I started to feel overwhelmed, like I was closer to losing my sanity than gaining it. I needed a break; needed to cut myself some slack, dangling from a string over these mountains and mountains and mountains of shame, pain, blame. Sick in a room, nothing but rain. Time to open the doors and let the sunshine in, literally and figuratively.

My guitar teacher, Ray, would soon be going back to school and working part time for a computer company. He wouldn't have time to teach anymore.

The only reason I remained in Toronto was the cottage we rented on Lake Ontario for the month of June; a nice little place — three rooms with a lovely view.

Rode up to the cottage tucked snugly between blankets, clothes, pillows, and food, in the back of the maroon Ford Taurus my dad purchased the month before.

The June summer had just begun, but you couldn't tell by the weather. It rained, drizzled and poured; lightning streaked the sky.

The cottage was going to be my sanctuary, a magical place where all I learned over the previous months came together; a place where, by water's edge, I would explore the mysteries of nature and find peace in solitude. I would live alone on a deserted beach, because during the week my father worked, and the weekend crowds returned home to their lives in the city.

Just me and the birds, me and the locals — a handful of people scattered around a deserted little town, where the main store (the only store) was smaller than a 7-Eleven.

Perhaps I was building the whole cottage thing up a bit, pretending I would find more than a month's stay on a large polluted lake could possibly offer. Yet at the same time, I was looking forward to stepping out my front door onto the cool evening sand and playing my guitar at sunset; looking forward to stepping out my front door to a light morning wind, taking a walk along the shore, stretching my limbs under a blue summer sky, basking in the sun.

The owners painted the cottage blue/grey with white trim — Cape Cod style — but the furniture was early 60s. Vinyl chairs. Something you might see on *The Wonder Years*. There was no phone, or television, the only amenities a refrigerator, a small gas burning stove to cook with in the kitchen, a couple lamps, and a large picture-glass window in the living room that overlooked the lake.

I put my things down in the guest bedroom, twin beds with sprung-out spring mattresses and floral print sheets. My dad and his new girlfriend, Brenda, took the master bedroom, which wasn't much of a master bedroom except that it contained a double bed with some poorly hung faux-wood paneling.

Still, the place had charm. I was a little disappointed that it wasn't just me and my dad. The year before we stayed in the same beach house for a week and had a great time. Now my little sanctuary had become their cozy weekend getaway. One more example of the way in which my dad took our quality time and crafted it into a love-in for him and his new babe.

Of course he didn't see it like that, and can't say I really did either (most of the time anyway). But, there's nothing worse than feeling like a third wheel to your old man and his new squeeze.

The Wilderness

Brenda was kind and I enjoyed her company. She was a registered psychologist and loved to play cards. Solitaire. Gin rummy. Spades. She had two daughters — eleven and fifteen — and on weekends when they came up, we all played cards together.

Actually, her fifteen-year-old daughter, when she came up, usually came up with a few friends. They stayed in another cabin we rented for the weekend, listening to punk rock on their Sony ghetto blaster from dusk to dawn, and doing whatever it is fifteen-year-old girls do when they hang together at a cottage on a lake in South Ontario.

Hanging out, I was cordial, kind, and friendly with Brenda, but the buck stopped there — me being the *buck*. Fact is, didn't really want to have much to do with her. Wasn't prepared to repeat the situation with my father's previous wife. I kept my distance, guarded my space. I worked hard to establish my boundaries, separate from my mother, separate from my father. Was just trying to make sure I kept them intact. Wanted no friendship that overlapped my dad's relationships, which, based on experience, seemed unstable at best.

Like I said, my dad and Brenda came up only on weekends, and worked during the week. When they came up, my dad and I found time between the time he and Brenda spent together, which was fine except it just wasn't the same.

While I enjoyed their company (even invited my guitar teacher, who was my friend at this point, up for one weekend), mostly I looked forward to the weekdays — the days when no one else was around.

Each morning I walked down to the water, a mere fifty feet from the front door of our cottage. To the south, following the lake shore, houses lined the beach. Heading north, the sand crept through a maze of tall pine trees that stood on the boundary of a large public park, where families came to picnic and play.

Wading through the water, I would alternate my route, going north one day, south the next. I liked to watch the sea gulls heckle and banter, competing for stingy scraps of putrid apple core.

Along the way, I found peaceful enclaves, where I felt no one would disturb me. Sat down, legs crossed, and faced the horizon settling in for an hour-long meditation. I started these meditations listening to the sounds of the water lapping the shore, the wind, and the gulls. That was how I started my mornings. The rest of the day I spent reading, lounging, listening to music, writing, and playing my guitar. If I got lonely, I hung out with the young family staying in the cottage across from ours.

Steve was my age. His wife, Monique, a year younger. They had two kids — Justin and Steve Jr. They took walks on the beach just like I did. Lounged in the water, just like I did.

"Hey, you play guitar," Steve said to me shortly after we met. "I brought my synthesizer with me. Perhaps we can get together and jam one of these afternoons."

"Sounds great."

Though we jammed only once, we spent a lot of time talking about the music we liked, and compared books we read. We talked about the differences in our lives. He had a family at twenty-three, something I could not fathom. I had been sick for three years, something he could not fathom.

In talking to Steve and his wife, I realized we had all come to this place to get away, regroup, collect ourselves before moving on to something else.

Out at the beach I didn't dwell so much on the fact I was sick. If I did, my thoughts did not consume me, because there was nothing to compare myself to. No people living lives I myself could not live. For the first time since school, I was doing exactly what I wanted to do.

I left Toronto in mid-July, a week after my father's fifty-first birthday. My last few days in Toronto were good ones. Said my goodbyes to the people I met — my guitar teacher, my therapist, my stepbrother, his girlfriend, and the city that brought me so much learning and struggle.

Before I left, we held a ceremony to celebrate my leaving, and to celebrate my induction into adulthood. Sounds sort of corny, and maybe it was. But it was something I will always remember.

We shared dinner at my father's house, my father and the other men from his men's group. Afterwards we gathered around candles grouped together on the living room floor. For two hours we shared stories about growing up and coming of age; stories about being stripped of victory at the moment of triumph, our dignity the only thing intact. We talked about what these moments meant to us, and how they changed our lives.

At the end of the night, each one gave me an object, something of significance that made a difference in their lives, then shared some final words of wisdom. One gave me a poem, another a song, another a key chain with a worn rubber wheel he carried with him during a period of hardship in which he contemplated suicide. There were words on it, words like, "I am forever, an ocean of consciousness, more than my experiences. I am one with God."

As we said goodnight, I thanked them for their gifts and felt full, complete. I was ready to leave. Like Max in *Where The Wild Things Are*, I sailed the torrid seas, landed on foreign soil, roared my terrible roar, gnashed my terrible teeth. I was headed home again following an extended stay; home to a warm dinner; home to face the shame and pain of my illness. I was ready now, no longer a boy afraid. I was an adult, crowned King of the Wild Things.

Part 3:

The Fruit

Chapter 15

Los Angeles. Land of opportunity. Beautiful beaches that stretch for miles, as far as the eyes can see. Jagged mountain tops. Sunshine all the time, except sometimes during winter, when you can ski the snow white slopes of Big Bear in the morning, drive a couple hours and find yourself at the State Beach jetties just in time for an evening surf session.

A city built by visionaries who channeled waterways to make lush an arid desert, then planted fruit trees to feed the masses.

A great melting pot. People from every race, religion, economic and social class, interacting, cohabitating, working together to build lives — to build futures.

Or are they divided instead? Rich versus poor. Black versus white versus brown versus yellow versus red versus ... blue? Everyone demanding a voice, demanding to be heard, demanding justice, protection, rights, and freedom without compromise.

A city that once epitomized the American Dream, now deteriorated into a postmodern industrial disaster. Polluted. Overcrowded. Overextended and out of synch.

People rushing, you can see it in their eyes. You can see it as they walk/drive by: rushing through warm sunny days; rushing through cool summer nights; rushing through life; through this money-image-status-conscious town, where those that live in small stucco houses leverage their futures on late model sport utility vehicles and dreams of becoming a star; and those that live in large stucco houses cruise town in late model sport utility vehicles glad to be one of the lucky, one of the few who don't give a damn about anybody but themselves.

Sure, I'm exaggerating — some people care. But L.A. is cold and hard, too mixed up in fantasy to recognize what's real; too overbuilt with quick and dirty fastfood joints, shopping malls and video stores to hold much appeal beyond the facade. You wonder, where is all this going? What are we trying to achieve? We're just perpetuating a bad thing, when the only thing that matters is stature, wealth, and "look at me!"

Arrived back at LAX on a Wednesday warm night in July. Standing next to the carousel, waiting for my luggage, I was admiring a young French girl — back-pack, doing the cross-America trek in a floral print mini and white worn tennis shoes. At least that was my vision of her. I was working up the courage to offer her a ride from the airport when my mom walked up.

She walked passed me two or three times without recognizing me — me in my long brown hair hanging past my shoulders.

"Mark, it's you!"

"Hey, Mom."

"I barely recognized you. Do you have all your luggage?"

"Yes."

"Okay, I'll get the car."

As she got the car, I carried my bags to the curb. I remember thinking she looked different, too. Her hair seemed lighter, longer. She was glad to see me, glad I was home. Yet, things were awkward at first. Didn't know what to expect. We hadn't spoken in some time, when I called somewhat into the blue and told her I would be home in two weeks.

Things were different. I was older. I changed a lot during the year I was gone. Didn't just look different, my values were different, my beliefs turned upside-down. I was road-weary and distant from a long hard struggle in

120

Toronto, during which many of the people I cared for let me down. And held me up.

While my mom was someone I could count on, someone I could trust, I wanted her to know things were not the way they used to be between us. I wasn't going to be her little darling any more. Despite the fact I would be living with her, I wanted her to know I was an adult.

The pathetic irony. A young man wanting to be on his own, trying to find his way, yet here I was completely dependent on my parents for financial/emotional/interpersonal support.

First thing I did when I arrived back in Los Angeles was re-do my room. With some of the money I had saved up, I bought a large futon to replace the twin beds I slept on since childhood. I bought two large pillows, and a bedspread to match the artwork which I changed, too.

Like a mini facelift, I replaced the collegiate banners and trendy posterboard prints with the stained glass and watercolor paintings I created while living with my dad in Toronto. I pulled out several old unused paintings and quilts from my mom's storage closets brought by my parents from trips to Asia and Central America many years before, and hung them in the room.

In the glass-paneled alcove towards the back of my room, I placed objects and trinkets — a miniature bronze Shiva, a Guatemalan flute, and the arrow given to my parents by a shaman who said it possessed magic. Do you believe in magic? Crooked with a dull wood tip. But, choose your prey and launch the arrow, the creature falls dead in its tracks. Gotta be careful with magic like that.

The second thing I did was contact Social Security. I wanted to have my own money. Money was always an issue in my family. Worth more than its economic face value, it was a way of showing love, structuring control. Just one more thing holding me back, keeping me down. Didn't want to feel like a burden to my parents. At the same time, I wanted to have some autonomy over my life. Money meant independence. Money meant being able to take care of myself. Money meant freedom from all the little things money meant beyond a basic means of common egalitarian exchange:

Money like love when the coins are drop clankin'
in the palms of your hands,
here's a little for the movies son
and little more for the clothes you wear;
like love when the dollar bills are slap, swackin'
the palms of your sweaty hands,
here's a little for the arcade son
and a little more to get you there;
like love when the fancy check
name scrawled in the bottom right hand corner
arrived each month in my rusty mail box, squeak creakin'
one more hug from mom, a kiss from dad.

Money like love that shake breaks me
as they saddled me with guilt for gifts I could never repay,
so that I might go mouth droolin', lip crackin' hungry
before I asked them for one more dime
before I had to listen to that smack bleedin'
pain in their voices — you had so much,
still a little was always too much;
like love so I wanted more just the same
a junky jail breakin' heart in search of a fix
hurt when it did not arrive,
because Money was all you could give;
like love so that when every last pinchin' penny spent
the caring gone, too, and the only river between us dry
like a dusty desert emptiness
and still all I wishfully, wistfully wanted
was to hear the words you could never say just once —
I love you.

So I called Social Security, filled out forms and followed up on the necessary requirements. After ten long months of waiting, I received my first check. With back-payments it amounted to five thousand dollars. Saw this as my chance, my first step towards financial independence.

122

The Fruit

In my eyes, I earned that money. Sitting in the Social Security office, following procedure upon procedure, subjecting myself to government scrutiny — all my finances monitored, my legitimacy questioned. I had been sick for three long years — I deserved it.

You can't tell me the people who live on Social Security are getting a free ride. There's nothing free about it. It's humiliating, degrading, unsettling, a royal pain in the ... foot. It's nothing any self-respecting person would choose to be on. It's too bad there exist those few recipients of SS who take advantage of the system. Milk it. Taint it. Paint it with a bad name, because most people on it are on it for a reason, barely getting enough to subsist, let alone live.

I'm not saying I'm ungrateful. I'm not saying that the six hundred dollars I received every month didn't help me out immeasurably. All I'm saying is that, given the choice, I would never choose Social Security over another source of income.

Judging from the looks on the faces of people who sat beside me on sweltering August days, no air-conditioning, heat too hot to move at the Social Security office on Sunset Blvd. — the Joneses, the Jeremiahs, the Janowitzes, the Jimenezes, and the Ji Bok Kangs — people living in virtual poverty. Maybe they felt grateful for what little they had, but not one of them felt lucky to be there, felt grateful to be on the dole —the government in control of their lives.

There's a toad under a stool and a stool under a toad, on a marsh near a road in Tallahassee. Met a young woman in the weeks before leaving Toronto. She suffered from chronic fatigue like myself, had been sick for several years, but was largely recovered and worked part time for *Keeping in Touch* — a newsletter written for chronic fatigue sufferers.

Her name was Tamara. I called *Keeping in Touch* to get a subscription to the newsletter and agreed to let them survey me regarding my illness. She was the person who surveyed me.

First time she called, we talked for about an hour, sharing stories of our uncommon struggle. Over the previous two years several people suggested I join a support group to share just this type of interaction, but I balked at the idea, in part denying the severity of my illness.

"Most of the people at those support group meetings are really sick. I'm not *that* sick. Been feeling better, really I have. It would just be a waste of my time," I'd say to them.

Balked also because I felt depressed about my illness; my tumble fall from society at large; my should have, would have, could have beens. I didn't feel like listening to a group of fellow sufferers complain about their losses, too.

Meeting Tamara, I realized it wasn't like that. She was someone who could relate to my struggle; someone I didn't have to convince that, while I looked completely fine, I didn't feel fine. Once I explained to people I didn't feel fine, I then had to go on and explain why it was I didn't feel fine.

"So, what's it like?"

"It's like a severe case of mono."

"Oh man, I had that for a whole month. Man, did I feel like shit. Couldn't get out of bed or nothin'."

"Yeah, well it's a little different than that."

"Couldn't you just sort of jog it out of your system? You know, just force yourself to get better. I know a guy who had something like that, sick for like two months. He just told himself, he wasn't going to feel sick anymore. Mind over matter, that sort of thing."

"Yeah, well it's a little different than that."

"Damn, just can't imagine being sick for three years. What's it like?"

Least he asked. Most people don't. They just think it's some sort of mental deficiency — couldn't cut it in the real world. With Tamara it was different. Everything I said, she responded to by saying, "I know. Tell me about it."

She would then offer a story in return, and it would be my turn to say, "I know. Tell me about it."

While it was unusual, Tamara agreed to meet me at my dad's place for lunch. At noon the following Friday, I answered her knock at my door to see her smiling face, and long black curly hair. She wore light blue jeans and running shoes, carrying a knapsack instead of a purse.

I prepared a large salad, the usual — lettuce, tomato, cucumber, grated carrot, assorted sprouts, baby corn, mushrooms, red bell pepper, green onion, and parsley, topped with garlic Italian dressing I made myself, accompanied by a loaf of warmed whole grain bread.

We sat out on the patio, ate and talked for two hours. Had a great time. When it came time for her to leave, I said goodbye, thinking I probably wouldn't see her again.

It wasn't that we didn't enjoy each other's company. Rather, I was leaving for Los Angeles the following week. I didn't think I would have a chance to see her again, so I merely felt lucky to have met her.

She called two days later and asked if I wanted to go to the park. Again, she came over. The park was just down the street. We walked and talked and laughed and lay in the grass. A large maple tree provided shade from the heat. Young kids played water games in the wading pool, while their parents talked to other parents and offered guidance from park benches around the perimeter.

"Be careful Tommy."

"Tina don't run, you might slip and fall."

"Maria give Ludwig back his ball. Did you hear me? Give Ludwig back his ball. I don't want to have to come over there. Now, give Ludwig BACK HIS BALL! That's a good girl."

The afternoon ended and we said goodbye. Again, I thought we wouldn't see each other before I left, but I called her a couple days later and she invited me to spend the afternoon over at her apartment. She picked me up in the pouring rain — a summer rain, warm and muggy.

Tamara wasn't working, but her father bought her a condo on St. Claire Avenue West, which she shared with her Siamese cat — Priestess, coy and distant. I watched Priestess watching me, as she sized me up from across the room. The stranger. Slowly, she moved closer, feeling me out, tuning into my energy to see if I could be trusted. Twenty minutes passed before she brushed up against my leg. Twenty minutes more and she rubbed her back up against my thigh. By the end of the day, I was scratching her behind the ears, rubbing her tummy a few times and we were friends.

Tamara and I spent the day lounging, listening to music — *Blue Rodeo* doing a live a show. It was the first full day I spent with anyone other than my dad in over six months. I felt human, as if I was part of something, part of life as we laughed, talked, entertained and ate pizza — cheeseless pizza, but pizza just the same.

It was getting late, so she took me home. The rain had stopped. We said goodbye. I was leaving the following day. We promised to write. I stepped out of her car and into the night. Tail lights, red glow fading, she disappeared down the street

I was home in Los Angeles about a month, when Tamara called. "I'm coming out to California to visit my father," she said. Her father had a house in San Diego. "He's only going to be there with me a week. Do you want to come down and spend a few days with me once he leaves?" Swimming pool. Sunshine.

I said, "Sure. That sounds fine."

She picked me up on a Friday with the agreement I would take the train back. Didn't know what to think, or what to expect. Were we just going to be friends? I wondered.

I hadn't been intimate with a woman in a long time, or even dated for that matter. Sick for three years. It's hard to meet someone, when you spend your days cooped up in the house. When finally you do get out, it's hard to project any real confidence, because you know you're limited. And when you see someone you might be interested in, the first thing that comes to your mind is:

"If she knew how sick I am. If she knew I don't have the energy to go to parties, go bike riding and mountain climbing — enough energy to maintain any kind of consistent lifestyle at all, the type of lifestyle the rest of the world calls 'normal' — she wouldn't want to go out with me. I would only be a burden to her."

So, I'd look away when someone, anyone, came my way.

126

The Fruit

If that someone smiled at me in passing and I had the chance to smile back, I'd try to pretend I was normal. Never revealed my little secret that I wasn't normal, not in my mind anyway, which left me most of the time feeling undesirable.

But there was more to it than that. Before I got sick, seemed as if I always had someone around, a girl I was dating. Usually I had a girlfriend — sometimes even a girlfriend *and* someone else I was dating, but not often. Just a young guy, afraid of commitment, trying to sow some oats. We can't all be mature enough at age sixteen, eighteen, twenty, to stay "faithful" to a single partner; buck the peer pressure, which in some circles tells you that to be a man you gotta lay a lotta babes and tell a good story about it when you're done:

I remember that quenching moment of victory
Saturday afternoons on Strawberry Field in Berkeley,
we were men playing a game for boys
we were boys trying to be like men.

With the game won,
we huddled around rank kegs of luke beer
drunk, obnoxious, belligerent,
we were men acting like boys
we were boys trying to become men.

We wore our battle wounds like trophies
on our scarred young and virulent bodies,
as the night drew on we hungered
hungered for the wet and wonderful world
of warm young women,
that fragrant plunge, loveless exploitation
(we could not recognize the exploitation of ourselves)
we were men playing the games of little boys
we were boys trying to find acceptance
into the world of men.

Looking back, I don't regret the things I've done —
just a healthy young man, having some healthy fun.

Except it wasn't always that healthy. It saddened me to think the intimacy I shared with some girls/women was cheapened by the failures of my emotional upbringing. Nothing wrong with making love, or sharing sex. It's when sex is power, when sex is just gettin' off and it doesn't matter whose legs lay spread canyon-wide beneath you. You're just grinding away, laughing at the day, not even thinking about the people you betray, when the person most hurt by your numb loveless sex is you.

I saw this as my chance, not to right my wrongs, but to recapture the spirit of intimacy in my life — to start again. I'm not just talking about sexual intimacy, but emotional intimacy, too. I wanted things to be upfront, everything clean like a stretch limousine, passion pure, nothing held back.

Most of all, I wanted it to matter: my friendships special; my love relationships cherished, in that they be built on a history of honesty and trust.

Sometimes living imperfect lives, we create/imagine perfect worlds, which is probably what I was doing as I pondered what might happen between Tamara and me. In fact, I was probably pondering too much, thinking and rethinking: "Is this right? What's it going to be like? What do I want out of this relationship? Are we going to have a relationship? Aren't we just friends? Could we be lovers? If so, what kind of relationship could we possibly have — she living there, me here? Do I want anything to happen at all? Am I ready? Will she be ready?" Obsession. Obsession.

Frankly, I wasn't even sure anything would happen. All she'd done was call to invite me to San Diego, two friends enjoying a four-day getaway. Not to get away from jobs we didn't have, or commitments otherwise binding, but simply to escape from being alone for awhile and to share good company, which wasn't always easy to find.

I slept for about an hour on the car ride down to San Diego, soaking in some tunes, the sun hot on my face. Why do the first hour-and-forty-five minutes always seem to fly by, while the last fifteen minutes stretch the dawns of time, until you're a man trapped in a steel-glass box screaming to get out?

I'll tell you why. I had perfected the technique of meditation in transit, deep breathing and a serene state of quietude to conserve my energy. Except by the end of long trips, I was like a ship about to explode, a man stuck in an extreme state of control. She's breaking up. She's breaking up ...

Managed to maintain composure and smother my desire to scream as we pulled into the driveway of her father's green, wood-and-stucco house, with an interior in early 70s decor. Yellow leather chairs and a shag carpet, with some late 70s tossed in for good measure. Silver wallpaper and a king-sized bed with rattan headboard and endtables. "Hey, turn off the Bee Gee's while you're up — *Charlie's Angels* comes on in five minutes!"

Still, who was I to complain? A summer heatwave had pushed temperatures into the high nineties. The air-conditioning felt good on my face, back, legs, arms, thighs, and buttocks.

Set my stuff down in the master bedroom, where I would be sleeping. Tamara was already set up in her own room. Threw on my trunks and headed out to the pool, where we lounged, swam, and drank iced tea, while we floated on blow-up pool rafts, talked and shared our version of the world.

In return for Tamara picking me up and buying most of the groceries, I agreed to do the cooking. Given that I was vegetarian and liked to cook for myself and others, cooking was more reward than sacrifice. With the day slowly fading, I went inside to prepare dinner.

Tamara bought a variety of vegetables, grains and fruits from the market before I arrived — zucchini, eggplant, tomatoes, tofu, brown rice, couscous, carrots, peppers, yellow squash, cantaloupe, apples, pears, mango, pineapple, grapes, and a basket of blood red plums.

For about an hour, I washed, peeled, diced, boiled and simmered, while Tamara cleaned and set the table out back. We sat down to eat just as the sun set, offered cheers and laughed at what a great day we were having — we the sick, the tired, who didn't have to work. It was Tuesday, mid-August and dinner was awesome: ratatouille, couscous and julienne carrots simmered in a honey-mustard sauce; the stars, like popcorn, popped up in the darkening sky.

With dinner and the dishes done, we sat outside beneath the night. I brought my guitar with me to share a few of my songs, which I sang as she sat on the chair next to mine, listening. Nothing like a good strum after a satisfying meal. Yet, I couldn't wait to put away my guitar and get close to her. The tension had been building between us all day, the wonder of what might happen.

Most of my life I had been pretty smooth with girls and women. I knew what to say, and when to say it. Yet, at this point, I felt nothing short of incompetent. It had been so long, I lacked confidence. Felt like I was back in seventh grade, when the first girl I kissed, Jill Glickbarg, had to kiss me. She cornered me on the stairs in Warming Hut 2, while skiing Mammoth Mountain. There was no place to run, no place to hide, but ready my lips and close my eyes.

Tamara and I were just sitting there, talking about this and that. I remember being really nervous. I kept thinking, "Now's your chance man, say something. Say anything. I don't care, but kiss this woman. Not ready. Not ready. Okay! Not ready. Now!" Which is when, at long last, I stumbled and bumbled and finally blurted, "Can I touch you?"

"Touch me where?" she asked, a concerned and somewhat embarrassed look on her face.

"I mean, uh ... um ... do you mind if I sit next to you?"

"Okay."

Wind, stars, moon, bright, wish I may, wish I might, held her hand first, then held her tight. I kissed her once, kissed her twice. She kissed back. I put my arm around her waist and pulled her closer, closer, caressing her olive skin, soft in the pale light.

When we walked inside, I felt butterflies in my belly, everything thrown into slow motion. I knew where we were going, knew what we were going to do. As we lay down on my bed, my body came alive, tingled. Yet, I didn't attack her. Took my time to taste, feel, touch and remember everything. I cherished everything, every moment, every instant.

I explored in ways I seldom did before, every inch of her body, massaging her, as she went down on me. Then reciprocating, I went down on her, and she caressed me. Still, it wasn't enough. I wasn't satiated and wouldn't be until I experienced her completely.

"I'm going to put on a condom."

"Okay."

"I want to be inside you."

"I want you inside me."

We were up most of the night, and tired all the next day, but it was worth it. Felt like wine lush grapes on a vine, my day ripe with pleasure, plush with congruence. Food tasted better than it had the day before. As I sat outside, the sun seemed to soak deeper into my skin. With warm sweat dripping down my face, I plunged into the pool, and the cool water soothed my body more content than Caesar spoonfed, white marble, and a satin bed.

Late that next afternoon, Tamara floated on one of the blow-up plastic pool rafts. I could sense her mind racing, as she stared at the water — reflections in the pool. I asked her to come inside, said I wanted to talk.

"Okay, I'll be in, in a minute."

We sat down on the bed in her room.

"So, what's up? What are you thinking about so fervently?"

"What do you mean?"

"Out on the raft. You just seemed as if your mind was churning, your thoughts cookin' away."

"How'd you know? I was thinking about a friend of mine back in Toronto. We went out the other night and he said he wanted more from our relationship."

"Did you ask him what he meant?"

"Yes, he said he wanted to go out with me. Now I feel all weird about it. I wish he never would have said anything, because I don't want to go out with him and I don't feel like we can be friends anymore."

"What are you going to do?"

"I don't know. That's what I was thinking about."

Before I left the following day, Tamara and I talked about our time together and how much it meant. It had been a long time since she shared herself, too — the bits and pieces, thoughts and smiles, hugs and holds. We were both glad to be back in touch with our sexuality, glad it happened with each other.

I stepped on the train, the conductor calling me guitar man.

"Hey, guitar man. What kind of guitar is that?"

"It's a Martin."

"That's a good guitar. I've got a Taylor sitting at home."

"So you play?"

"Twenty years."

"Wow, that's great."

I looked out and saw Tamara crying. I knew it would be a long time before I saw her again, which was something else we talked about — the distance and the difficulty of maintaining a relationship three thousand miles away. Made me cry, too, over the sadness of having found something so beautiful, only to lose it so quickly.

We promised we would write and we did, long revealing letters — eight, nine, ten pages at a time — a mixture of poetry and tear drops dried on the page. We weren't in love, but we cared for one another deeply.

As the months passed, the writing and waiting time between letters grew — one week, two weeks, then a month. Found time to write when we made time but letters got shorter, six pages then four. That Christmas I sent her a card five sentences long:

How's it going, Tamara? I've been writing quite a bit, working on my children's book. I'm still writing poetry, singing and playing guitar. L.A. is alright, but I don't know how long I'll stay here. Hope things are well with you in your world. Merry Christmas!

*C*hapter 16

It's crazy when the world caves in, crazy what you could have been. I need this. I need this ...

The few months following my trip to San Diego were good ones. I grew healthier, with a healthier perspective on life. Still, the struggle to regain my health continued, which made it clear I wasn't ready to go back to school. Didn't want to face the struggle of attending school and worrying about my health, so I didn't force it. Decided to hang out, continue to take walks and spend my time writing music, poetry, and children's stories.

I was writing and illustrating *Mr. Mistor, Buster & Pfister*, when I met Alex:

> Mr. Mistor is the master painter of Keyster Beach, Mississippi. He likes to paint crazy things, clowns that wear bonnets, dogs that wear rings, big smiling faces with bright shiny teeth, buildings with hands, baseballs with feet. He paints anything. He paints everything. He'll even paint you.
>
> Mr. Mistor has a sister, Miss Mistor, who is the elementary school teacher in Keyster Beach. She teaches the alphabet from A to Z, how to count the numbers past three. She'll teach you to touch your toes, while standing on one foot in the pouring rain. Everyone says she's the smartest. Some think Miss Mistor's insane.
>
> Every year Mr. Mistor and Miss Mistor get together for Easter dinner at the mansion Mistor Manor in Middletown, Mississippi. The mansion's

133

not haunted, but something's not right, creatures are always stirring, and the bed bugs really bite.

Mistor Manor is the mansion of Doctor Mistor and Mrs. Mistor, the mother and father of Mr. Mistor and Miss Mistor. While Doctor Mistor is quiet, patient and full of neighborly cheer, Mrs. Mistor is neurotic, wild and sometimes even a bit weird. But the Mistors are happy and have lived in the Manor for many, many years.

On this particular Easter, Mr. Mistor and Miss Mistor arrived at Mistor Manor, home of Doctor and Mrs. Mistor, for dinner just a wee bit early. Since Easter dinner was not yet ready, Mrs. Mistor, who loves to play *Twister*, asked them to gather in the main room of the Manor for a fun and friendly family game.

In the backyard of the Manor lives the Mistor's dog, Buster. Buster is bulky and brown with black big eyes. He spends most of his time digging ditches for bones and sleeping under the pine roof of his home — Buster Manor — built especially for him.

Doctor and Mrs. Mistor also have a feisty feline named Pfister. Pfister likes to play with string and partake in catlike things — napping, purring, jumping, and touring through the wonderful wild beyond the backdoor of the Manor.

But together, Buster and Pfister spell terrible trouble. Buster loves to chase Pfister all over Mistor Manor and does so for much the same reason the Mistors play *Twister* — for fun. Even though Buster is bigger than Pfister, Pfister is faster than Buster. To this day, Pfister has never been caught. So, while the Mistors were playing twister, Buster was chasing Pfister, and all of a sudden Buster and Pfister came bursting into the main room of the Manor and ran right through the Mistors' game of *Twister*.

Well you can imagine what happened when Doctor Mistor went diving after Buster, and in so doing tripped over Miss Mistor, who then fell on top of Mr. Mistor's leg, but not before Mr. Mistor managed to knock over Mrs. Mistor. Until all the Mistors less Buster and Pfister were sprawled on top of the game, *Twister*, in the main room of the Manor just moments before Easter dinner ...

The story goes on and is resolved in that upbeat way children's stories generally are. Maybe I was a little out of synch with my audience, a little over the top for their ages two to four-year-old minds. But, most kids like wacky things. I know I did growing up. I sure had fun writing and illustrating the story — hapless Buster, sly Pfister and the rest of the Mistors, varying takes on the same expressions and gestures. They looked like some cloned-out 50s family with their neurosis meticulously cloistered behind collared shirts, glasses, golf hats, and bonnets.

Alex was my mom's friend. They had previously worked together at the same public television station. Alex was much younger than my mom and their relationship was more mentor to mentee than tight personal friends.

Alex had been married a little over a year to a man more interested in the computer chips he designed and developed than he was with her. Theirs was an abusive marriage, not physically, but emotionally. Her husband put and dragged her down, until finally he broke her.

They slept in separate beds, in separate rooms, in separate parts of the house. She was depressed, clinically so — self-esteem sucked right out of her, day-by-day, her husband stealing her life away. She had a hard time finding a job after they moved from southern to northern California, her husband following employment in Silicon Valley. She had a hard time keeping the job she finally did find. She was confused, alone, and at times could barely get out of bed. She felt her life was over, as if it walked out from under her and she'd lost all connection to reality and to herself.

I was eating dinner quietly as Alex and my mom entered the house, returning from dinner themselves. I knew she was coming. Knew a lot about her actually; my mom always raved about her gorgeous young friend. I even knew what she looked like. We had a picture on our mantle of her and her husband marching down the aisle on their wedding day; smiling on their wedding day; happy, holding hands on their wedding day.

"Mark, this is Alex," my mom said as they passed me

in the dining room.

"Hi, Alex it's nice to meet you."

"It's nice to meet you too, Mark. I've heard so much about you from your mom. I feel I practically know you already."

"Yeah, me too."

"Well, Alex and I are going to retire to the living room to start drinking. Why don't you come and join us when you're done with your dinner? Alex will be staying with us for the night."

"All right."

Alex seemed very nice and attractive — blond hair, blue eyes, charming smile — which I noticed, but made no real note of. She was my mom's friend come down from northern California, staying the night.

They drank red wine in the living room, laughed about old times, and were sharing stories when I walked in to join them. Alex brought pictures of her dog, Ralph, the little house she built for him, and the furniture she stripped, stained, painted, and refinished in her spare time.

Like show and tell, I shared pictures, too. Pictures and drawings from *Mr. Mistor, Buster and Pfister*. It was a fun night. We had a good time. At 10:00 p.m. I stood up and said, "Good night, it was nice meeting you, Alex."

"Nice meeting you too, Mark."

"I'll probably see you in the morning. Good night, Mom," I said, then headed upstairs to bed.

As a young man, I often fantasized about an older woman slipping into my life and passionately seducing me. I sold home video delivery service door-to-door during college, solar heating panels door-to-door during high school, hoping one day the door I knocked would be opened by some nymphed-out undersexed vixen in a satin bathrobe — hot and steamy, just out of the shower:

"Hello."

"Hi, I'm with Murphy's Express, the home video delivery service ..."

"Sure is hot out today."

"Yes, it is."

"Why don't you come inside for a moment and I'll give you something to drink."

"All right."

"How does an ice cold beer sound?"

"Perfect."

"Are you hungry?"

"Starved."

"Put your things down and take a seat over there by the couch. I think I've got just the thing to *satisfy* you."

Yeah, right. Never happened. Closest I came was an old lady who one day offered me some lemonade for carrying a particularly large planter box clear through to her backyard.

"Such a nice young man, would you like some lemonade?"

"No, that's all right."

"But, I insist. You must have something, how about some cookies and milk?"

Guess I saw *The Graduate* one too many times growing up. I was a young man searching for Mrs. Robinson behind every door. Or maybe it was all those pornos I used to watch as a kid. Which is why, wonder why, I thought little of Alex that night.

This gives an idea of the way I physically felt. I was tired and down again — struck, slip, stumbled again. Winter was approaching, encroaching on my sanity. Nowhere to turn, but in; nothing to see but ...

We woke up the following morning. Alex was leaving that day. She and my mom were going to breakfast, so I mustered the energy to join them.

Over breakfast, Alex talked about her failing marriage, smiled occasionally, frowned and saddened mostly. She was so attractive, so intelligent, so absolutely charming, yet like my life, a dark cloud lingered over hers — a rain cloud building that would soon burst. She came to Los Angeles, looking for a way out. She couldn't pretend any longer. She couldn't uphold the facade of the perfect life, the perfect wife — everything happy, funny, comfort and plenty dropping in droves from trees and vines.

She left after breakfast to visit her brother in Orange

County, both to spend time with his kids and to straighten out some unresolved family issues, but returned later that same night. I walked downstairs to get some water and saw her talking to my mom in the dining room. Things had not gone well with her brother.

"What's wrong Alex? Are you alright?" I asked.

"Oh Mark, it was horrible, but I don't want to talk about it," she said, seeming very upset.

"That's okay. I'm sorry things didn't go well with your brother." Then I gave her a hug and said, "Well, good night. Maybe you'll feel like talking about it in the morning."

"Maybe."

I was leaving to take my walk the next morning when Alex said she wanted to talk to me about something. My mom had left for work. Alex would be leaving too, heading back up to the Bay Area and I assumed she wanted to talk about her brother.

"Sure. Do you mind if we walk and talk about it?"

"Okay," she said.

We walked up the cement cracked streets past shrubs of bougainvillea and ivy to the edge of Griffith Park, where we sat down in a vacant lot that overlooked one of the canyons in Los Feliz and started talking.

"So, what happened?" she asked, referring to my illness.

"Well ..." and I told her the story of my three-year struggle. I told her all about my mother, my father, my father's ex-wife, as Alex sat, patiently listening. Occasionally she asked questions to clarify things I was vague about or overlooked. What I liked most about Alex when we first met, was that she wasn't put off by things I told her the way most people were; people who had never taken time to glimpse beneath the surface of life — the dingy, soggy underbelly that, when revealed, caused them to stiffen and smile uncomfortably, like I told them too much; people around whom I'd find myself back-peddling, "Oh, I guess it's not that bad. Anyway, did you see that movie about ..."

After we talked a while about my life, we started to

talk about hers, living in the Bay Area — the unhappy wife of a man she didn't love, didn't like, couldn't even stand to eat dinner with. We talked about her family, her dog Ralph, and the struggles she encountered recovering from a longterm eating disorder.

I began to feel close to her, as if I found a friend to confide in. In between our conversations, I thought about how I hoped our friendship would develop and wondered if I would see my new friend again once she left. Then she said, "You know, I feel really close to you Mark. I've found it's not often you find someone you can really relate to, like the way we're really connecting here. Do you think you could ever consider me more than just a friend?"

"What do you mean?" I asked. But, I knew what she meant. I could tell by the way she said it, just didn't want to confront it. What do you say to that? What do you say to a woman who's your mom's friend, but who's totally amazing? She's married, but looking to get divorced and has a personality that makes you feel like you could spend forever with her and never get bored.

You say no, of course. Am I right? Of course. Well I didn't say anything. Just got up and started heading back down the hill, not talking about what she just proposed, or even dealing with it. Yet, it was there. Our discourse changed course, because I knew something about her I didn't know an hour ago — a secret I didn't want to share, because it seemed too sexy to be true.

Back at my house, we sat around and talked some more. My mom came home for lunch. She was surprised, but pleased Alex was still there. We all ate together, sat out on the terrace, me with salad, they with sandwiches, overlooking the sunshine-splashed hills and the city below. We all laughed and talked until my mom returned to work. Alex and I were alone again.

She and I migrated to my room. She wanted to hear the poetry I wrote and talked so much about — me sitting on the edge of my bed, she kneeling on the floor next to me. How close would we get? How far would we go? I opened my notebook and read:

sometimes, when in my private hell
I feel so weak in the world around me,
I need to be held
curled up like an infant
in reassuring arms all around me;

letting go, let go
cry swollen tears
and for a while feel at peace,
safe from this struggle that surrounds me day-to-day
it never seems to completely go away;

someone to hold me tight,
someone to hold me in my fright,
someone to hold me deep into the night,
protection in their arms
from the world, all around me.

    As Alex listened, she edged closer, first leaning against the bed, then sitting next to me, later lying down. After a couple hours we were both lying down, staring at the woodbeamed ceiling, my comforter scrunched beneath us, feet hanging off the side of the bed, listening to music. She turned to look at me and I looked back. Then she said, "Can I kiss you Mark?"

    "That's probably not a good idea," I said still fighting the confusion; fighting the fact she was married, my mom's friend, ten years older than I. Ten minutes later:

    "Can I kiss you Mark?"

    "No, I can't, it's just not a good idea. I'll hold you if you'd like."

    Man, was I sap. Man, had I lost it. The old me would have dealt on her and have done with it — would have had a little fun, a little hit and run, then walked her warmly to the door. The new me should have known better than to land myself in the middle of something so complicated. Yet, there I lay, stuck between two me's, somehow swallowing the notion it was okay to lay on my bed caressing my mom's friend and yet it wasn't okay to kiss her.

    "Can I kiss you, Mark?"

"No."

"Can I kiss you, Mark?"

"No."

"Can I kiss you, Mark?"

"Well, maybe just once. Maybe a little more." And there I was, the ordained prince of proper giving into temptation like a Madonna virgin, *touched for the very first time.*

She was delicious, so tasty, sweet. We kissed for a long time, warm hands on hips and skin, holding each other tight. But, the day was coming to close and it came time for Alex to drive home. We didn't know when we'd see each other again. How quickly we'd become more than just friends. She couldn't stay another night, or even hang around to have dinner with my mom — too much heat, synergy, guilt. We had stumbled into that grey area of comfortable, where comfort beyond merely ourselves was difficult to predict.

She gathered her things — her suitcase, her long brown coat, the little packages carrying the few items she bought while visiting, her diet Pepsi, and a couple poems I wrote. I helped her out to her car.

"Don't go," I found myself saying.

"I have to."

"Why do you have to?"

"I don't know."

"Then don't go," I repeated and all that sort of corny stuff, before we hugged, kissed and said goodbye. I watched her drive off, then walked inside to think about the day and all that transpired.

*C*hapter 17

Turn of the century: populism fed into the progressive era and this was the birth of the big city; trust busting and the big "Bosses" in Chicago; W.W.I.; race riots; women's suffrage and the first Red Scare. Then came the Roaring 20s: flappers and the Harlem Renaissance; buying on credit; the dawn of the jazz age and prohibition; then the stock market crashed on Black Monday.

The 30s inherited the Depression: hobos on box cars; families living in shanties and the beginning of the welfare state. In the sleek 40s, we met fly boys over Hitler's Germany, the baby boom, the arsenal for Democracy, Bob Hope and Scarlet's Tara burning into the 50s: the Cold War; McCarthyism; Ozzie & Harriet on TV, as the CIA spread its arms around the world; roast beef and mashed potatoes; living in the suburbs; Motown and the "American Dream." The 60s paved the way for moonwalks, Camelot and the counterculture, civil rights, the anti-war movement, Woodstock and *the summer of love* before the 70s: Detente; the end of the Gold Standard; the beginning of disco and bell bottoms; gas lines; Watergate and America's disillusionment with government.

The 80s brought us the computer age, New Age, junk bonds, the debt crisis, supply side economics, break-dancing, and Tears for Fears. And so far in the 90s, we've seen communism crumble, the information age begin — telecommuting, the Internet — Seattle grunge, the Religious Right and their conservative backlash, the

The Fruit

backlash by liberals against the conservative backlash, the progression of AIDS, and the dismantling of the welfare state.

Where is it going? Where do we go from here? War. Mass starvation. Overcrowdedness. The underprivileged. Is this just a cycle? In the late 20s the world's banking system collapsed, the U.S. stock market crashed; many were jobless, some homeless, when the world erupted in war. Are things worse or better today, getting worse or better tomorrow? Who created this machine? Who's perpetuating it?

At every turn, there's a new scene, a new dream, a new idea. If we were five hundred million people living in a sandlot, someone would corner the market on sand. We're creatures in a human world — building, creating, destroying, perpetuating, living, working, dying, breathing, eating. Everything alive — dead, then alive. Waves of consciousness — a current to describe our existence. Think about it:

Wind currents. Ocean currents. The tectonic plates shifting. Blood streams. Electricity. Streams of thought. Evolution — time passing as a progression into the "modern age," like a glacier carving its way into the 21st century — a current. Brain waves, microwaves, radio signals — all currents in our current conscious experience. Currency. Life like a current, spinning on a ball circling the sun, caught in a gravitational pull within a larger solar system that had begun by the biggest wave of energy ever recorded — the "Big Bang," a bang so big it can still be heard fifteen million years later echoing through the universe. What the fuck am I talking about except that God has no face. God is like you and me; is a current. God is everything — God is in us. Religion has it all wrong, we are God, dog, the Force, whatever you call it. This ain't going away. We humans may die out, but we as dog will live on in a stream of peace and unrest ...

early morning
rain once again falls quietly past my bedroom window
I feel at the same time lonely
and peacefully complete.

143

Dazed And Fatigued

I wonder, as I lie rumpled in bed
staring at the darkened sky
if the swanlike nuances that shift these clouds,
shift too the thoughts in my mind
the feelings in my heart —
intertwined on a loom of experience
where moments are woven, one to the next,
yet always shifting, always changing
so the pattern is never fixed or secured
but always resembles itself.

    This was the gist of the first letter I ever sent Alex. When she opened it, she was hoping for a love letter; hoping I was writing to tell her how much I missed her and ached to see her. Instead, she got a long confusing letter drafted in furious blue scrawl on plain lined paper torn from a notebook.

    "What is this?" she asked over the phone.

    "It's about currents. The idea that all life, the entire universe — physical, spiritual and otherwise — can be summed up as one big current, where God isn't a deity, but the current itself and in this manner should be loved and appreciated."

    "Yes, I understood that. Why did you write it?"

    "I was reading *Illusions*, the book you gave me. I've been searching for a metaphor to describe what I've learned about life and there it was in the opening sequence. You know the beginning — when Bach talks about those village creatures clinging to the bottom of a crystal stream, resisting the current?"

    "Yeah."

    "One lets go and the others laugh and tell him he's a fool, that he'll die, but he does it anyway?"

    "Right."

    "Then, as he floats downstream he comes across other creatures clinging to the bottom. They say, 'See! A miracle! A creature like ourselves, and yet he flies! See the messiah come to save us all!' I realize the message is something altogether different than my idea of life as a current, but it was the story that inspired me."

144

"But, what do currents have to do with anything? What do they have to do with us?"

And so we went round and round. It wasn't that she didn't understand the concept, or that she didn't agree with it, or that she hadn't shared the same thoughts at least on some level herself. Rather, she couldn't understand why, of all things to send her a letter about, I would send her a letter about *currents*.

Maybe it was a bit weird, but I felt inspired. Felt I had something to say, something to share. I wasn't writing so much to foster a love relationship I had doubts about to begin with. I was merely writing to share my thoughts with a new friend.

The truth is, Alex and I didn't always see eye to eye. We shared many of the same thoughts and ideas, yet our perception of reality differed. Our perception of what was important at what point in time and how to spend that time differed to the point of dichotomy. What do I mean? Let me show you.

We talked on the phone daily, two lonely people sharing inflated phone bills. Alex was out of work, at home, alone, but for a few hours each evening her husband was home and then they spent their time in separate rooms. I, too, was out of school, out of work, removed from the common routine of life. We talked about thoughts large and small, issues of import and inconsequence, this, that, chit-chat, misery, pain, joy.

It sure seemed a sordid set-up to say the least: she, long-distance living in northern California — married. Still, the most difficult issue to confront was that Alex and my mom were friends. For the first few weeks, we talked a lot about whether a relationship between us could work:

"But you're married," I said.

"But, I don't feel married, and I'll be getting divorced soon," she said.

"What about my Mom?"

"What about the fact that I feel so much older than you?"

"Ten years, it's not that big a deal. The distance is what I'm worried about. When I started Berkeley, my girlfriend went to Menlo. We never even saw each other and she lived a little over an hour away. How is this going to work between us with you living in northern California?"

"We can talk on the phone. I'm not working, and we're not that far away. We can see each other once a month."

Great, just what I needed. I was already vulnerable, tired — and now the torment of a long-distance relationship. I had the pleasure of going through my first long-distance relationship with my high school girlfriend, then later my college girlfriend — relationships too difficult to maintain. Snivel, snivel on the phone; snivel, snivel via packages and letters.

"I miss you."

"I miss you, too."

"I love you."

"I love you, too."

Snivel, snivel, torture, and longing, until they failed after a few short months. Each time they failed, I promised myself, "I'll never do that again." Was I crazy? Was I an idiot — a young man who has lost his capacity to remember how miserable long-distance relationships were?

Maybe it would work this time. If it began long-distance, maybe I would know no better. Maybe I was alone. Maybe she was amazing. Maybe I didn't care.

"Mom, there's something I have to tell you. I don't think you're going to be happy about this, but I wanted at least to be up front with you — you know — honest, so I don't feel like I'm hiding anything from you."

"You're moving back to Canada?"

"No."

"You're going back to Berkeley? Mark, I want you to go back to school, but ..."

"No Mom, I'm not going anywhere."

"Then, what is it?"

"Alex and I want to start dating. We really hit it off while she was here. We've been talking on the phone pretty much every day."

"But she's married."

The Fruit

"I know, and believe me I'm having some problems with that, too. But she's unhappy in her marriage, and she's going to be getting a divorce."

"But she's my friend. I don't want you dating my friend."

"I know Mom, I'm sorry, but it's something we've talked about and we want to give it a try. Which brings me to the second thing I wanted to talk to you about."

"What's that?"

"She'll be coming in about two weeks to spend time with me."

"Where's she going to stay?"

"My room."

The audacity — what was I thinking? Yet, what choice did I have? Knew my mom wouldn't be happy about it. More than that, I knew she'd feel betrayed by her friend, and by her son. But, if it was going to happen at all, my mom would have to know — we lived in the same house.

That night I felt both guilty and elated. Told my mom and she didn't completely freak out. She'd get used to it. Alex was a friend of the family, why not bring her into the family? Right? Yeah, right. Alex was coming, that's all that mattered.

She came down on a cold Friday night in early November, green socks, green shirt, suitcase in hand. I opened the door to all kinds of expectations, as we walked up to greet my mom. They drank wine by a warm fire, sharing laughs and more stories. Only this time, Alex came to see me. It was weird, downright awkward, when at the end of the evening we said goodnight, walked upstairs to my room, set down her things and readied for bed.

It was also weird, because I barely knew her and yet here she came to spend the weekend with me — a shared understanding, we were standing at the edge of some kind of relationship about to jump off and dive in. Where would the relationship go? Where could it go? We didn't know.

She undressed to a t-shirt and underwear, brushed her teeth and climbed into bed. I joined her in my plaid boxer p-jays, my cold room made sharing a warm bed all the sweeter. She lay beside me, music playing. We kissed, undressed some more. It felt good. It felt right. I wanted everything and nothing that night. Then she said she wanted to make love.

"How can we make love if we don't love each other?" I said.

"Why can't we have love for each other without being in love? And why can't we make love without being in love. Do you love me?" she said.

"No."

"Do you have feelings for me?"

"Yes ... ?"

Man, was I easy. Man, was I scared; afraid of what I was feeling; afraid of the way my body shivered. I held her tight as she caressed my face, my arms. Such a beautiful smile, so much charm. Who was I kidding? I wanted to make love more than she did. Slipped her panties past her feet, slipped myself naked, slipped in deep — deeper than I had ever gone. Shivering. Quivering. So much to feel, so long empty ... hollow — now filled. I felt everything, like a watershed — joy, sorrow, bliss, tomorrow. I touched her everywhere, as she touched me. Closed my eyes smiling and slipped into sleep.

Chapter 18

With my newfound friendship, my spirit was reborn, my sense of mission and purpose renewed. I was on a new quest to find the medical/non-medical — whichever it didn't matter — miracle to cure my malaise. Part of my reason for returning to Los Angeles had been to try a detoxification program I heard about through my friend Siubhan.

Siubhan's mom was bedridden for about a year when she stumbled into the program designed to eliminate pesticides, herbicides, chemical compounds and metals found in the soil, air, water — toxins like lead, mercury and DDT; eliminate them slowly from the body.

I was aware of people who suffered from environmentally-related illnesses. Their bodies so overrun with environmental toxins that they were exhausted, laid out. Some had grown highly allergic not just to certain allergens, but to life in general. Lived in plastic bubbles, oxygen tents and traveled around in earthbound astronaut suits — glass bulbous heads with big funny boots.

I subscribed to a newsletter put out by people who suffer from environmental illness (EI). I often related to the stories written by people whose friends, family, and neighbors would say things like:

"It's all in your mind. Look, I grew up next to a nuclear reactor and you don't see me complaining about environmental toxins. Just take a walk outside, take off that funny mask, set aside that silly oxygen tank. This time things will be different. You'll see. It's all in your mind."

149

Wish it were so. Wish it were all in my mind, then maybe I would snap out of it. Yeah, I could relate, 'cause it's all the same. It's all related to the stresses of a techno-logically advanced, humanely bankrupt society. Pollution. Fast food. Fast cars. Long hours. Too many people, living too close together. Ozone holes. Crazy weather.

For $3,500 (actually, $1,200 if you did it through the Church of Scientology), they purified your body to its core, starting you out on a treadmill to raise your heart rate, then sticking you in a temperature-controlled sauna — five minutes the first day, and ten the following week. By the end of three months you're running for half an hour, then spending half an hour in the sauna, sweating and purging, drip-by-drop, every pollutant ever introduced into your body.

It wasn't the money that stopped me from doing it. Any amount of money was worth spending if it meant having my health back. Nor was it that I had something against the Church of Scientology and their belief in a man that created the largest/richest cult in history (next to Catholicism).

Rather, I questioned how polluted my body could be given all the vegetables I ate, the purified water I drank. Sure, there are pesticides used in agribusiness. Sure, traces of some toxins could be found in my body. But I suffered from something virus-related. At least I felt I did. What if the detoxification program made me worse? Five minutes on a treadmill would wipe me out — thirty might kill me.

I was working with a new doctor, Megan, a family practitioner familiar with and open to alternative medicine therapies. Started seeing her in relation to the detoxification program. She worked extensively with the program and was the one who would have cleared me for treatment at the Scientology Celebrity Center.

She was a Scientologist, but never really talked about it or made an issue of it. She was just a great doctor. She treated several people with illnesses similar to mine. Wasn't ready to detoxify, so I started exploring other treatments

150

— more vitamins, minerals, and amino acids.

Finally Megan sent me to another Chinese herbalist, a woman who literally saved her life sixteen months before. Megan developed a rare case of meningitis of the brain (yet another crazy fun illness. Where do they come from and who's thinking all this shit up? You can just hear the sound of the pharmaceutical cash register, *"ka-ching"*). Doctors said there was nothing they could do for her. Said she'd be dead within six months. After one week of seeing the herbalist, she was fifty percent better; after two weeks, eighty percent; and after a month she was cured — what a beautiful word.

Like so many stories I read about, stories I heard, people finding miracles every minute of every day in every corner of the globe, except mine, I had to believe I was just a treatment away. I had to believe luck would soon take a turn my way.

Alex took me to my first appointment. Needles hooked up to wires sent an electric charge pulsing through my body; glass bowls left suction welts black and blue on my back. I had to drink herbal teas made from pods, leaves, roots and seeds — teas that tasted so bad, I could barely force them down, down, down the hatch and through my veins. I imagined it purging the illness from my blood.

After three months of treatment three times a week, nothing was happening. Wasn't getting better. Plus, the treatment was expensive. Wasn't covered by insurance. I decided it wasn't worth the time, money, stress, dress-you-up and strip-you-down — lying on a cold table, needles and pins in my skin, my free hand plucking dollar bills from my billfold.

I started looking into really alternative treatments — treatments being developed and tried in Europe and South America, research on the cutting edge. With some back-ended reasoning, I figured if I spent a lot of money on some wild treatment only meant for those who could afford it, maybe then my fate would change; that the action of spending alone would reflect my commitment. Once my body/God knew how committed I was to healing, it/He/She would allow me to be healthy again. I was subconsciously suggesting that, up to this point, I hadn't been committed enough and therefore had not been worthy of realizing perfect health. Quite a heavy mind game!

I heard about a therapy in which ozone (O^3) was injected into your bloodstream slowly over a period of a couple weeks. I read testimonies to the effect that this treatment was curing AIDS and all kinds of rare, otherwise untreatable diseases, because disease cells could not live with O^3 present in the bloodstream.

I read about shark cartilage crushed to form a powder, then turned into an injection that was curing cancer because of the shark's rare immunity to cancer cells.

Then I heard about Marvin, who was running a program in Mexico. He claimed he was curing cancer and other chronic illnesses; claimed he was working on a program to cure AIDS. Alex read about a woman in the paper he cured of chronic fatigue. She gave me the woman's phone number, who in turn, gave me Marvin's.

When I called him, Marvin seemed like a smart man, but he was making some wild claims. Couldn't tell if he was legit or insane — a freak, with a freaky name. I asked my doctor Megan if she would talk to him, probe his medical jargon for me. She called after speaking to him, "You know, I think Marvin sounds like a pretty smart man."

"Do you think his program might help me?"

"I don't know, but you seem pretty determined to try out one of these programs and Marvin could be onto something. There's a lot more experimental medicine available to the public down in Mexico. Not all of it is good, but this could be. I'd say if you want to try it — try it. Let me know what happens. If it works, I may have a few other patients I could send to him."

I talked it over with my parents and decided the $3,000 treatment would be worth every nickel and dime if it cured me. So I cashed in some childhood bonds. I was going to Mexico the week between Christmas and the New Year, having chosen Marvin as the means to my miracle.

My mom and I drove down to Tijuana on a Wednesday and met Marvin in a Banco de Mexico parking lot just across the border. He was strange-looking, tall and wiry, with salt-and-pepper hair, glasses, and a quirky, jerky walk — like a chicken or some long bird.

Marvin, like myself, had been the victim of a strange illness that left his body paralyzed for over a year. Actually, his body was more like frozen. He had lain in bed, a tube in his mouth; some virus had seized his circulatory system. Can't quite remember how he was cured, or the name of his rare disease, but remnants of the illness still lingered, like his funny walk and his skin that wasn't soft and stretchy like normal skin.

"Touch my skin," he said to me.

"What do you mean?"

"Just touch it."

So I touched it. And he smiled and said, "It's not like normal skin is it?"

"No, it's not." In fact, his skin was smooth and hard like plastic. "Why is it like that?" I said.

"It's part of the illness I had. For a while my entire body was frozen stiff. Now it's just my skin. I'm hoping even that will go away, as I continue the treatment you'll soon be on. The treatment rejuvenates your cells at an accelerated rate."

"Feel that," he said as he flexed his arm, making a muscle. "I practically never work out and I'm healthy as an ox. You're going to be like this, too. You'll see."

He tried to put me and my mom up in a high-rise luxury hotel room in downtown Tijuana that was a dark, depressing twenty stories above the ground — nothing nice about it. However, as I looked out the window and down, I noticed a two-story hacienda-style hotel. We checked it out and discovered the rooms were larger, brighter, and — does this surprise you — cheaper. I decided I'd stay there instead.

"The treatment is a series of twelve shots given over a three-day period," Marvin told me my first night there, where the intent was first to starve the virus, then annihilate it from my system. "There's one other shot that I am about to give you now," he said, as he opened his black medical bag and pulled out a series of long syringes and liquid-filled vials. "This is an inert bacteria that will serve as the focal point around which your white blood cells will gather momentum to combat the illness through your internal defenses."

"What is an inert bacteria?" I asked.

"It's a bacteria that's dead, but the body thinks it's alive. I'm injecting it just under the skin. Does that hurt?"

"Not really."

"This won't make you sick, but it will make your body think it's being invaded. You may see a large blister on your leg tomorrow. Don't worry about it, it'll go away in a couple days."

He made it sound like a game of Stratego, or some Hollywood silver screen remake on the Battle of Waterloo. It sure sounded like a great idea, like it might even work — thick shots, with long needles, severe and painful into my backside. Yowwch!

After the first day of treatment I could barely sit, my butt black and blue, with a festering sore of inert bacteria on my right thigh. My mom and I sat in the hotel room watching reruns of *I Love Lucy*, as it poured rain outside. At ten o'clock the next morning Marvin returned. "How do you feel?" he said. "Notice any change in the way you feel?"

"Not really, no."

"Did you walk around at all today?"

"No. Not really."

"You should get out, and don't worry — you'll start feeling better. Some people feel better the first day, others feel better the second. Most feel better within the week. One guy came down, felt nothing; called me after a week — still nothing. It got to the point where after month he actually started demanding his money back, then whammo! It hit him. He woke up one day and he was cured."

"Really?"

"Yeah, but you have to be patient. Sometimes there's been quite a bit of damage done to the cells. You've been sick quite awhile."

"Three years."

"That's right. Your body doesn't just heal overnight,

which is why we give you the capsules. Sometimes even after you've knocked out the virus, it still takes time to heal the cells."

As he reassured me and gave me my next round of shots, Marvin went on to divulge many of his theories on life. He saw conspiracy in everything. The government perpetually harassed him with charges of fraudulence. The American Medical Association kicked him out because he was dangerous — he supposedly knew too much. He knew that for years, AIDS research had been headed in the wrong direction, same with cancer treatment. Yet, there was so much money in it, so many doctors making money under currently funded cancer research programs; pharmaceutical companies making money off AZT and chemotherapy; a road so long traveled it was too late to turn back even though failure was imminent.

He talked about conspiracy in business. He said the US government and US corporations were really the ones behind Japan's booming economy; that they owned most of the Japanese industrial complex. He said SONY stood for "Standard Oil of New York."

It was all very fascinating. Marvin was fascinating, as he sat back in his chair, an arrogant grin stretched out across his saurian lips, weaving tales of corruption and greed. Maybe he saw a slightly distorted view of the world. Maybe everything he said was true, or half-true, so that it rang true that night. Every time I thought I found a flaw in his reasoning, Marvin had an answer for me. He had an answer for everything. Marvin was either a genius or he was completely nuts, but Marvin was a great guy. He believed what he was saying. He believed in the shots he was treating me with, that he could cure chronic fatigue, cancer, and some day soon, AIDS. For a while, I believed he could, too.

Over the next three days, Marvin came twice a day. Each time he came he'd ask, "How are you feeling? Feeling better? Maybe you just can't tell, yet. Did you try walking outside?"

While I envisioned myself getting better over a series of days, Marvin actually believed I should be feeling better overnight. Not just a little better, but totally better, like I'd just snap out of it — like someone standing in the dark who suddenly had the lights turned on. Said he'd seen it happen, that it happened all the time with most of his patients undergoing the same treatment. Said even if people aren't totally cured they at least start to feel better.

Which was when I realized the treatment wasn't working for me. The minute he lowered his expectation and started setting me up for "feeling at least a little better," I knew things weren't going as hoped or expected. Which was when I wished I could have my money back, but it was too late for that. I paid Marvin the night I arrived, up front and in cash. I had to believe the treatment was going to work.

When I arrived back home, Alex came down to visit. She said I looked different.

"But I don't feel different."

"I can see it in your face. There's more color in your skin — more glimmer in your eyes."

"Really?"

"Absolutely. Something about you has definitely changed."

"Guess I just can't tell yet."

From L.A., I kept in close contact with Marvin. Kept asking him when I would start to feel better. I began taking the colored capsules — part two of the treatment — three times a day. Then I nearly collapsed while walking one day. I felt dizzy, an out-of-body sort of dizzy. Started breathing deep and hard. It couldn't be the water — the Mexican water they warn you about in campy beer ads. It had to be the capsules, so I stopped taking them.

When I told Marvin what happened, he suggested I drive back down to Mexico. Said he would give me six more shots at no extra cost. I would take the shots back across the border with me, which, of course, was illegal. Yet at this point, I would have gladly steered a boatload of hash up from South America if it meant getting my health back.

This time, the drive down felt a little easier. I even felt a little better when I arrived in Mexico than when I left

L.A. Marvin, my mom, and I traipsed around, tracking down the glass vials of liquid used to fill the shot syringe I would administer myself. We stopped at the clinic, where several cancer patients were being treated — patients who looked as if they wouldn't live to see the Tijuana sun set behind the bleak brown hills the following day. We picked up the vials, then I drove home to Los Angeles, where, after three more weeks passed — still no change — I was stuck with the fact that something else would have to work. Three thousand dollars down and more than a little disappointed, I realized Marvin's treatment had failed.

*C*hapter 19

Despite my inde*fatigable* — isn't this somehow ironic — search for a miracle cure, I actually started living again. Back from the dead, lost, empty. I experienced my first New Year's Eve out in over three years — dinner at a vegetarian restaurant on La Brea with Alex, who looked so amazing that night I couldn't take my eyes off her.

Alex spent quite a bit of time with my mom and me during the holiday's. Where was her estranged husband? What was he doing? Don't know. Didn't ask. I just felt lucky to have her around as we decorated the tree, burned logs in our fireplace and listened to Christmas music — burnt embers crackling time to duets that combined French horn with classical guitar.

With the new year kicked off, I started working a part time job that was about as part time as you can find. One hour a day, maybe two, from the privacy of my own home. I started selling syndicated news columns geared towards teens for another one of my mom's friends who was in sales and in need of some assistance.

A little background: the fallout of the new media-driven information age is that less and less people are looking to printed material as their prime source of information and entertainment. Why read a raggedy old newspaper, when you can just pop on your box? Listen. Watch. Have the entire world transported into your living room via television, a satellite dish, and your home computer.

While a few noteworthy adults are currently leading the technology push into the next millennium, an entire generation of children spend their afternoons playing Nintendo64 and Sega Genesis, surfing the web for that vital piece of information they need for their school science project.

Truth is, the Internet may prove to be one of the most significant developments of the 20th century, despite the hype, fanfare, and overblown expectations of the fortune seekers still panning for gold amidst cries of "Eureka!" A networked brain that spans the globe, heightens our consciousness and sense of context; that helps us to recognize we are connected, not just on a physical level through food chains and evolutionary development, but on a conscious level as well. At any moment in time, we can log onto a computer somewhere and find out what people are doing in another city. We can find out where the action is in another country, on the opposite side of the planet; information at our fingertips — omniscience personified.

In February, I traveled to San Francisco to visit a good friend from college. He lived with his then long-time girlfriend in an apartment complex on Sutter Street, just east of Filmore near the West End.

They were both in law school, chasing dreams that no doubt made their parents happy and proud. They were good, decent people. In a way you might say I was jealous of them — the happy young couple on their way to happy comfortable lives with high salaries, a townhouse and a couple of BM'ers parked in the garage. Two kids. Two dogs. A swimming pool, and them looking down their noses saying, "Mark, you've got to get your life together." As if it were my fault.

Maybe at that time some part of me felt it was, even though I know better than to believe that now. It made me want to say, "Look, I was the honors student in college. I was the one who studied while you partied; achieved, while you got by. I'm no urban snowflake." So, I said it.

But it didn't matter, especially not to Chris, who, because he was one of my best friends, just wanted me to have my health back. He pushed and bantered and asked questions about what I was doing to get better, because that was his way. And I pushed and bantered and held him off with answers that sidestepped his accusations that maybe I wasn't doing enough to get better, because that was my way. In the process, we had a great time.

Alex drove up from Atherton for a few hours each day to spend time with me before returning home again that night. Seven days, six nights I spent hanging out in San Francisco. I ate Chinese food in Chinatown, took a motor-cycle ride through Golden Gate Park, walked the Haight, and saw *The Crying Game* at a theater filled with arthouse misfits. Jay Davidson, you bastard! Just as I finished telling Erin, Chris' girlfriend, what a babe I thought Dil was:

"At Berkeley, I used to know this black girl who looked just like her. She was so sexy. I love that look. This girl is so hot." Then, two scenes later — "No Way!" — turned out she's a he and man did I feel stupid.

Upon waking each morning, I'd say goodbye to my two friends as they scrambled off to class. Alone in their apartment, but for the city outside, my mind opened to the possibilities of a new day:

Water — misty — floats in a glass mug
on a black table, in a gray room;

Light — hazy — filters through transparent windows onto
a striped couch set against a back wall;

The sounds of cars traversing in the street
below the morning cold
            and the day ripe for pleasure.

Old friends, new lover, in a northern town
overgrown needles yearn for a distant sky.

Winter feeding into spring,
a quiet adventure calmly ensuing,
and I am born
      into the world again.

The Fruit

Back in Los Angeles, I continued taking walks through the neighborhood, writing children's stories, poetry and songs, corresponding with Alex, and working:

"Hello?"

"Hi, my name's Mark and I'm with the BPI Entertainment Newswire."

"Yes?"

"Do you currently have a section geared towards teens in your paper?"

"No, but we're considering one."

"Really, that's great. Are you familiar with BPI —"

"Have you heard of BPI —"

"We have a teen advice column —"

"We offer a syndicated news service —"

"Do you get many entertainment photos —"

"We have a photo service, in which, each week we send you between ten and twenty photos digitally transmitted over the AP pictures wire — "

"Hi - my - name's - Mark - and - I'm - with - the - B - P - I - Entertainment - Newswire."

This all began at about 9:00 a.m. each morning after my walk, just another cat in the neighborhood come back to turn my hat tricks into cool cash — a dollar here, two dollars there, eat lunch, cat nap, then crank up my Mac for an afternoon session on the computer.

I was writing a children's story about a princess who had been a victim her entire life:

... The Princess Eisland had long dark hair and beautiful green eyes. Being a princess, she spent most of her time doing those things that make someone of her stature princess-like. This included: studying ancient and outdated foreign languages; studying the vestiges of foreign cultures and her own culture — extensively; and basically learning to walk, talk, sit, stand, ride, run(actually a princess can never run, she must glide like a feather on the wind), and dance with that subtle grace inherent to those of the royal crest.

All this training towards perfection left Eisland with no friends, for she had no time for friends.

When Eisland could find some free time to spend with her peers, the other girls in the kingdom and around the castle treated her as an outcast or someone to be avoided, because they were jealous of her stature, beauty, and luxurious fortune. King Brus, who felt his duty as king more important than his duty as father, spent his time absorbed in what he so frequently referred to as "matters of the crown" and had no time to spend with Eisland. So, even though Eisland had people around her every day — teachers, trainers, coaches, and servants — deep down she was very lonely, because she had no one she was close to.

One would never guess the princess was lonely by looking at her, for she concealed it beneath a facade of summer smiles and springtime cheer. However, this facade only exacerbated her intense loneliness, because it didn't allow anyone to share in her struggle. Instead of seeing Eisland's loneliness, all people could see as they stared at her enviously was perfection.

But late at night, while Eisland lay locked within the confines of her private chambers, she did not feel perfect at all. Instead, she would sob, and she would sniffle, and, as she stared out beyond her empty window sill, she would often wonder, "Is it I who cannot find happiness, or happiness that cannot find me?"

I started writing the story six months earlier, after seeing a picture my friend painted of a dragon with its wings wrapped around a young girl. Seeing the picture made me recall some of the books I'd read, like Sam Keen's *Fire in the Belly*, which made me think about innocence and naiveté; about the oppression of women in a society dominated by men; made me think about myself. Like the fact that it's important to be kind, but if your demon, that is your dragon, your fury, lies locked up inside your mind, you end up being walked on, put upon — a modern-day victim.

So my story was about a princess who knew nothing of her dragon, her power, the strength residing within her. This particular dragon, much like Eisland's inner dragon, was incarcerated in a mountain, locked up far beneath the earth. The dragon is so terrible, so feared by everyone in the kingdom, they deny it even exists, like some dirty, nasty, skeletal, family secret no one ever talks about.

My only problem with the story was that, while the men in *Eisland and the Dragon* were complex, multi-dimensional characters, the women, including Eisland, were vapid, bland, and lacked substance. I had no model for them, no voice I could steal or emulate. Sure, I had friends who were women. Obviously my mom was a woman. Yet, I was entirely unable to internalize female emotion to the point of making it my own.

That changed when I met Alex. She became my princess. I took her thoughts, interpretations, actions, reactions, emotive responses and transposed them onto Eisland, rewriting Eisland's character. At each point in the story I would ask myself, what would Alex say in this situation? What would she do? How would she respond? When I did, my story came alive. No longer about fictional characters, the story was about Alex, and about me.

The story was also about my father, my mother, and coming to terms with my own dragon. So as I wrote, I watched my own life unfold through the story. When divisive issues arose between Alex and me, I wrote them into the story, working them out through my characters, before coming to terms with them myself.

I was midway through *Eisland and the Dragon* when Alex and I broke up. It wasn't a bitter break-up. Alex separated from her husband, looking for her own place. Things really weren't the same after I returned from my trip to San Francisco. We hadn't seen each other in months. The couple times she was supposed to come down and visit, she didn't.

The last time she came through Los Angeles, she was on her way to Texas to spend time with her parents. She arrived two days later than she planned, went straight to a friend's house, and called me the next day, "Hi Mark, it's Alex."

"Alex, where are you? I thought you were coming straight here."

"It was so late when I drove down, I didn't want to wake you. I decided to stay with a friend instead. You're never going to believe what just happened."

"What?" I said, feeling dismayed.

"My car was broken into last night after I arrived. They stole everything, all my clothes, everything."

"No! That's terrible."

"The police are here now. The car is completely stripped. I'm going to have to fly to Texas."

"What are you going to do about your car?"

"I don't know yet, and I don't know if I'm going to be able to see you while I'm here. I'm leaving tomorrow and now with this ... Look, you can call me tomorrow if you want, but I don't know when we'll be able to see each other again. So, I'll understand if you don't want to call."

As she's talking, I'm thinking: first, she's obviously upset about her car being broken into and I should probably call her; and second, the sound in her voice and the way she's been avoiding me lately suggests our relationship is clearly over, so — why drag this on?

Like any young guy stuck on pride, I decided not to call her. This became the point in my story that Eisland rides her horse out onto the beach, not remembering she has asked Terron, her lover, to meet her there. When she sees him, she tells him she loves him deeply, but out of obligation to her father can no longer see him. She gets back on her horse and rides away. Terron, depressed and heartbroken, collapses into the sand crying, pounding his fists. Yet, when he's done crying, he reaches a point of forgiveness and supports her decision to leave him.

Yeah, right! Which is why I rewrote that part of the story. Forgiveness, while key to a peaceful life, is sometimes a tall order. I felt left behind, abandoned, betrayed, pissed off. I searched my mind for memories of days when Alex would say, "I miss you, Mark," over and over again.

She hadn't said that in a while. The day she went home to Texas it rained, or it was cloudy, or maybe the sky was clear and the sun shining. As I lay curled up on my blue bed, in my blue room, blue pictures and tapestries hanging from the walls, all I could see was a grey sky, grey clouds. I knew it would take me a while to let go, my tears slippery, sliding away.

164

*C*hapter 20

It was the year of Clinton. Ross Perot faltered from the perch of his "bully pulpit." George Bush's tongue tied up in his lips, and delirium left him murmuring something about a "thousand points of light." Left the Republicans reeling as the Democrats took control of the White House and the Congress.

In his State of the Union Address, Clinton called for a "New Covenant." He set forth the challenge of saving the Union with universal health care, safer streets, tighter borders, a clean environment, more money for schools and worker retraining, and a First Lady who wasn't a house-wife, but a corporate lawyer.

The beginning of a new era. The next generation. The "me" generation. Baby boomers, their poets and their Rhodes scholars leading the charge into the 21st century.

But, for every person who clamored — "Change!" — there were two who were afraid: doctors lobbying for dollars; families worrying about security in the face of corporate cutbacks, government setbacks; homophobes exposed in the military; gay rights, student fights, and multiculturalism left people demanding, unbending, unsure of an uncertain future.

Sure, I voted. But, I also sat back and watched as time and the world outside spun by. I was walking, reading, doing yoga, still meditating and becoming more strict in my vegetarianism.

The chaos, craziness and confusion I heard on television each night never seemed to find its way to my doorstep. As far as I experienced, despite what I knew, the only thing still wrong in my world was that I slept fourteen hours a day — still a manchild stuck out on the fray of society.

As summer approached and with Alex gone, I needed some new experiences to fill my time. I started frequenting a poetry group every Sunday from 3:00 to 6:00 p.m. We gathered at the Iguana Cafe in North Hollywood. Books lined the walls — Dylan Thomas, Jack Kerouac, and Flannery O'Connor inspired us, as we sat around in a semi-circle on couches worn comfortable, tables and chairs to discuss our writing.

They sold crystals, trinkets, muffins and drinks in what seemed a mini head shop as you walked in. A small stage was set up in the back for music and readings held nightly. We read our poems in turn as the others listened. When done reading, listeners critiqued and made comments on how to improve the words, the language being applied to thoughts and emotions.

The first time I went was the hardest. With each critique, however appropriate, I felt stabbed, slighted, like the father of a newborn child, whose doctor says, "Well, your kid isn't that ugly. Maybe with a little plastic surgery we can fix his nose, tweak his cheek. Just looking at him now, the poor thing's terribly incomplete."

More than a few people stormed from the room, like one man with his thou's, his thus's, his here ye's, and his cometh's. When it was suggested he try using modern English, he tucked his three-ring binder under his arm, swore several times, and vowed never to return.

"What was he expecting from us?" someone asked.

"Guess he wanted us to fall all over him," someone else chimed in, and tell him how wonderful he was, that he had conquered not only modern English, but middle and old English, too; that not since Shakespeare, Poe and Yeats have we esteemed such a remarkable poet — a master of his craft."

No one really wants to hear the truth. They say they do. What they really want are half-truths mixed with fiction

166

and a little honey for good measure. For instance:

"Hi, how's it going."

Well, my wife just left me. I'm suffering from a terminal illness. My dog recently ate my favorite pair of shoes, and my Jeep is in the shop again. "Good. And you?"

Which is why few people ever tell the truth, the whole truth anyway. The truth is, it would be inappropriate to tell the truth all the time. Why share your problems with someone who doesn't want to listen? Why hurt someone's feelings, when you don't have to?

"Listen, I don't really know you, but what do you think of my new hairdo? I want an outsider's opinion so to speak."

Actually, I think you look ridiculous. Probably be better off bald. "Yeah, I think it looks pretty good."

You've got to choose your moments. Which is what I did through my poetry. My poems were the one place I felt I could be completely honest; the one place my darkest secrets were revealed. I could sit down and start writing, tracing an idea or a thought only half-developed. When I was through, the words revealed an entirely new level of understanding within myself. Poetry was my catharsis, which made sharing it very difficult.

"They're going to see me — judge me by my darkest thoughts, my most deviant desires, my most intimate pain."

Yet, I quickly discovered that everyone else in the room, everyone reading, was sharing their most intimate thoughts, their darkest desires, their most private pain. It was like some self-help confessional for dysfunctional adults, but with a difference — it was beautiful.

Words and rhythms united to convey meaning. There were long discussions not on the content of the words, but on the words as a vehicle to reveal content. Heated debates over the placement of commas, conjunctions, definite and indefinite articles. I always walked away having gained a little insight, a little knowledge.

And then Victor joined the group — rather, he rejoined. He had been away or something, I can't remember what. He was an overweight, disheveled man with pockmarked skin and scraggly brown hair. Looking back, he was a good poet. Yet, as a man, he repulsed me.

His first day back, he read a poem bashing men; a poem of jealousy and rage towards men successful with women, where he had decidedly failed. It wasn't our job to criticize the content of the poem, just the words and the use of language. Yet, I felt so offended, as if the whole time he was looking at me, raging at me. The poem ended by essentially saying, "... and all they ever think about is their penis. Penis. Penis. Penis. Penis. Penis. Penis."

So, I said, "wasn't that a bit much? I think we got it the first time. Why do you have to bash us over the head with all those 'penis'-es."

"That's the idea," he snarled.

Wasn't long after the day Victor came back I stopped going to the poetry group. I just didn't feel comfortable and it wasn't just Victor, it was the whole scene, or unseen. I didn't know these people. While part of me wanted to know them, another part of me didn't. My confidence was low, yet my arrogance was still intact. I was quiet, shy, uncomfortably removed from the group, sitting in a room full of people I didn't understand, because I had nothing in common with them beyond poetry. They were the working class, the underclass, over-the-hill, under-the-mark, regular everyday Joes.

On some level I felt better than they were, shallow things like the fact I felt I had better schooling; that I had grown up with greater opportunity. Every time someone stood up and chastised the "system," I felt like I was the system. I was the white, upper middle-class male that went to private school, dated attractive women, drove fancy cars on long vacations that most people just talk about.

Yet, I wasn't that. Fact is, I was none of that — no sexy job, no sexy babe, no sexy car, no cushy life. I had no life. I was supporting myself on Social Security. The most important thing I did each week was go to that little poetry group in North Hollywood on Sunday and it wasn't good enough for me.

Made me wonder why it was that nothing was ever

good enough. I learned a lot, even grew a lot as a writer, but I wanted more. I wanted to cavort with great minds; discuss the pressing issues of our time — conversations sparked from ideas elucidated through tight coherent poetic verse.

I wouldn't just share my work, but give readings to an audience to inspire, teach, and feel what it's like to bathe in the glamour of attention.

Walked out one day and never went back. That was that. I thought about going back a few times, but each time something different came up. I was tired, too busy, had nothing new to share.

It made me sad I didn't feel I belonged in that group; sad I was too shy, too unaccepting to make real friends beyond the occasional, "wow, there was so much power in that. Your writing has gotten so much better. I don't feel like you're talking at me anymore, I feel like you're talking to me." Wondered if there were others who felt the way I did: uneasy as I walked through the door; unrecognized as I sat down with the sparkling lime Calistoga I purchased each week from the man who owned the coffee shop — Bill, Barry, Bob, can't quite remember what his name was. All I remember is that I didn't belong, and didn't make any real friends there.

When I stopped going, I didn't even join a group of great minds to share, discuss and hone my skills. I just kept on write-writing in the privacy of my own home; kept on walk-walking; kept on work-working. My summer came and as it went I was faced with a new development — my mom accepted a job in Washington, DC.

Chapter 21

My mom hadn't been happy with her job working for public television. She felt under-recognized, overworked, as if she were being taken advantage of. When the opportunity came for her to be president of a small company servicing public radio, she took it. Packed up and moved out, cross-country to a little apartment in Arlington, Virginia that overlooked the Potomac.

Before she accepted the position we talked about her leaving and the fact I would be living on my own; her concerns about me being able to take care of myself; my concerns about living alone, living in her house.

She couldn't/wouldn't sell the place. Called it her "nest egg for retirement" and knew that within a few years she would return to Los Angeles. She asked me to take care of the house for her. Hired a maid to keep it clean, because we both knew I wouldn't be doing much housework — not yet anyway.

The day she left, the world got larger, or I got/felt smaller, like one of those commercials in the late 80s:

"When you're all alone out there and you feel like there's no one you can turn to ..." They would feature a man lost at sea, a large shark fin circling his little yellow inflatable life raft. "Just pick up the phone and call ..."

Except there was no one for me to call; no one but my family and a few friends I called from time to time; no one but the editors I called trying to sell syndicated news columns; no one but the woman I worked for — my mom's friend. She was cool; she often supported me in my work and in my struggle.

"But that's all anyone has," she'd say, "family, friends, co-workers."

"Yeah, but it's different for me."

Isolation was a frightening prospect — the house empty of all things living with the exception of myself and a few plants. Did my grocery shopping via telephone for a little while — called up, ordered, and, for a fee, had food delivered to my door, up my steps, then set down in orderly fashion on my kitchen counter top.

I thought about getting a dog to keep me company, but my mom's allergic to dogs — she didn't want one in her house.

My days were quiet. My nights virtually silent but for the drone of cars driving by on Interstate 5 in the distance, the strum of my guitar, the company of my TV talking and the occasional beat of drums that rattle 'n' hum from the living room stereo.

here comes the evening, here it comes to me
here comes the darkness, the stars touch the sea
bring back the easy, tomorrow, and the song
who's that you're holding, bring her along

this is my castle in the sky
this is my castle on the edge of a stream
this is my castle in some angry dream

drive my chariot across the water's wake
this is my castle on a placid lake
this is my castle built of mortar and stone
this is my castle in the clouds all alone

this is my castle in the sky
this is my castle wonder why

It was like I inherited a small castle on a hill, with me its king, living the childhood dream of having my parent's house all to myself. How would I change it? What would I do with the house, now that it was mine? All those little, subtle things — ways I would make it better.

An Indian summer that year chased the heat into the fall, as the Santa Ana winds blew wildly through the valleys and over the hills. Great fires swept through southern California. Burning embers and sheaths of fire went out of control in Malibu, Laguna and Pasadena.

Arsonists started some fires, while others were merely the result of the dry season — careless men and women not realizing the danger of a smoldering cigarette butt, or a shard of glass from a broken bottle magnifying the heat of the sun onto straw grass, making it catch fire. One homeless man built a fire to keep himself warm during the night that he said, "just got away from me, like a slippery fish," only fish don't burn houses.

At dusk from my balcony I could see the flames rising over the hills of Pasadena — deep red against the backdrop of a cobalt blue sky. The fire was as beautiful, watching it from a distance, as it was destructive.

While I enjoyed my solitude, after a couple months living alone it became clear I needed a roommate to share space, time and the cost of my monthly utility bills. My mom was against the idea at first, didn't want anyone living in her room. But, she was paying rent on her apartment and after a couple months decided the extra income would offset the cost of the mortgage she was also paying on the house.

Dave was one of my oldest friends. We went to the same elementary school. From the time I was in eighth grade, our families were neighbors. We went to the same high school, which was unusual because it wasn't the local high school, but a private boys school over in North Hollywood. Our mothers took turns driving us to school until we grew old enough to drive ourselves.

For college, we both went to Berkeley, where we joined the same fraternity. It's not like we planned it that way, it just happened. I'm not saying Dave had nothing to do with me joining the fraternity he joined the year before

The Fruit

— he was a year older than me. But, Dave and I led different lifestyles growing up. We were good friends, but hung out in slightly different crowds. I partied to have fun, Dave partied to party. I played football and rugby, while Dave played basketball and ran track. I liked loud music, big crowds with lots of action. Dave liked louder music, small crowds and a different kind of action.

When Dave moved in, our lives were as different as night and day: he black, I white; he a meat and potatoes guy, everything fried, frozen and fast; I a strict vegetarian, nothing that wasn't off the vine preservative-free; he indulging in every vice known to man — smoking, drinking, random women and drugs on a regular basis; I an ascetic — meditation, no drugs, no love, Siddartha in a cement palace in the sky.

Dave liked living back in his old neighborhood, and gave up his single bedroom apartment off La Brea and Sixth Street in Hollywood. He liked having a big house, someone to kick back with, hang out, watch television and talk smack with.

I liked it too. Felt like I was back in touch with the children of my own generation. Dave's old friends were my old friends. As they called to talk to Dave, they started calling to talk to me.

"Mark, how's it going? Long time."

"Yeah, it's good to talk to you."

"Heard about your illness. How are you doing?"

"Still dealing with it. But, I think I'm starting to feel better."

"That's great, man."

"Yeah, it is."

Bottom line was, Dave brought energy, enthusiasm and fun back into my house, my life. As I saw the things Dave did, like staying out into the wee tiny hours, then getting up to go to work all day, playing sports, enjoying the fray, I remembered what it meant to be healthy; not just what it looked like from the viewpoint of an onlooker, but what it meant in terms of the lifestyle a perfectly healthy person could capably lead. I had been sick so long, I actually forgot. I witnessed the lives my dad and mom led, but compared to a young man in his prime — his energy level was awesome, something I hadn't seen in a long time.

Made me want it more. Dave was in the "real" world. I was in my own world, at times living vicariously through him.

"Where you going, Dave?"

"Out drinking. Think I'm gonna shoot some stick."

"With who?"

"A few friends."

"Sounds cool."

"Should be fun. See you later."

"Yeah, later."

About the same time Dave moved in, another friend of mine floated back into town and into my life, who shared some of my desires, similar ideas and dissatisfactions with life. Jay spent two years overseas, teaching English as a second language in a refugee camp in the town of Aranya Patet on the Thai/Cambodian border. He lived in Bangkok, writing news stories for the Far Eastern Economic Review. He spent some time in Manila with his father, who was then serving as U.S. Ambassador to the Philippines. In the same year he dated the daughter of a Philippine military general and a prostitute from the streets of Bangkok.

We barely knew each other in high school. We attended similar party functions and got acquainted at Berkeley. Spent the same summer in Washington D.C., interning on Capitol Hill, which was where we played tennis a couple times and started to become friends. But, it wasn't until I returned to Berkeley after withdrawing the first time that we really were what I would call good friends. We took yoga classes together. Went out to lunch and on walking excursions down Telegraph Avenue to have our auras cleansed by healers practiced in the "hands of light" technique.

However, we didn't stay in touch when he left for Asia. I didn't realize he went to Asia in the first place. I dropped out and moved to Canada at about the time he graduated, migrated back to Los Angeles, then skipped town — ten thousand miles away. Quite a skip, wouldn't you say? Maybe you'd call it a hop-skip, he traveled so far away.

When he returned, Jay heard through a mutual friend I lived in Los Angeles; heard I was sick, but writing children's stories, poetry and music. The day he called, I was both surprised and glad to hear from him. Said he was in town for a little while and that he wanted to stop by for lunch one day. I said, "Sure, that sounds great."

On his way over, Jay stopped off to see another mutual friend of ours working as a Hollywood agent for television and screen writers. He arrived at my house carrying two spec scripts, written by working TV writers — one for "The Simpsons," the other for "Wings."

"This is the worst, most unfunny, simple writing I have ever seen. We can do this. All we've got to do is follow the format. Let's write an episode of 'The Simpsons.'"

"Okay," I said.

He came over for a couple hours every other day. Probably would have worked every day on the script except my energy was low, like plowing snow, only it was the end of summer. I needed time to walk and get out of the house.

He'd sit at my computer, typing, I in the chair beside him, or lying down, eyes closed, firing ideas back and forth. Clickety-clack. Clickety-clack. His fingers on the keyboard, laughing hysterically. We watched episodes of the show, learning the characters, their quirks and idiosyncrasies. Within two weeks, we wrote a forty-page script about a relentlessly sexy young French girl eagerly pursuing Bart all over Springfield. Her father had been sent over from France as an environmental engineer to conduct a year-long safety and procedure inspection on the nuclear power plant, where Homer Simpson works:

CUT TO: MR. BURNS' OFFICE - DAY

Mr. Burns and Jacques Croissant are sitting around the table eating from a huge wheel of Camembert cheese, drinking Pelligrino.

SMITHERS
Mr. Burns, Simpson's here.

MR. BURNS

Who?

SMITHERS

Homer Simpson, sir, the man who lives
across the street from "Mon-shur" Crescent.

JACQUES

Pardon me, but that's Croissant.

SMITHERS

Uh, right.

MR. BURNS

Splendid, splendid, send him in.

Homer walks in and sees the cheese and crackers on the
table.

HOMER

Ohh cheese, and so close to lunch.
Don't mind if I do.

Homer reaches for the cheese and has his hand slapped
away by Mr. Burns.

MR. BURNS

Don't even think about it, Simpson.
The CamemBERT is for our friend,
Mr. Crescent.

JACQUES

That's Croissant.

MR. BURNS

Whatever. Mr. *Croissant* has been sent here
by the Global League of Waste Watchdogs,
otherwise known as GLOWW, to inspect
our plant.

176

HOMER
(still eyeing the cheese)
So ... I can't have anything to eat?

MR. BURNS
No, Simpson, you are here for the
explicit purpose of assisting Mr. Crescent ...

JACQUES
Croissant.

MR. BURNS
(cont'd)
... during his inspection of our plant.
He will be looking into our new,
world-class, waste-treatment apparatus
to make sure they meet global standards.
I am sure he will find everything
to be more than satisfactory.

Burns leers at Croissant out of the corner of his eye.

JACQUES
Well, we can only hope.

HOMER
(nervously loosening his collar)
But why me, sir?

MR. BURNS
Yes, Simpson. Excellent question. Why
you? We did a search through our
computer's employee files and discovered
that you have recently spent some time
in France.

HOMER
Yes, but ...

MR. BURNS

We think your knowledge of the French culture could be of great help in facilitating Mr. Crescent's inspection.

HOMER
(under his breath)

Oh, I see.

MR. BURNS

What's that, Simpson?

HOMER

I mean — Oui, sir. Oui.

MR. BURNS

Now, Smithers, why don't we take Mr. Crescent on the *official* tour of the plant. I want him to see everything.

SMITHERS

Everything, sir?

MR. BURNS

Everything. We have nothing to hide.

Burns leans on a button on the desk exposing a back room where employees are being tortured, then quickly closes it back up.

MR. BURNS

Oops. Right this way.

CUT TO: BART'S TREEHOUSE -DAY

Looking at Bart through the treehouse window, we see the large, red feather of his head-band rising up slowly into the picture, as Bart emerges, looking out of his binoculars.

BART
Bart Simpson, the Last Mohican, surveys
his terrain.

We look out through his binoculars with him.

BART
(cont.)
All clear on the horizon, all clear out on
yonder trails. Wait a second ...

In Bart's vision we see Millhouse and Clarisse Croissant
walking toward him.

BART
Oh, man!

MILLHOUSE
Look who I brought with me, Bart, the
beautiful and enchanting Clarisse Croissant
from class today.

BART
Halt where you are paleface. You speak
with forked-tongue. You've breached our
ancient bloodpact. No squaws allowed
on these premises!

MILLHOUSE
But Bart, Clarisse wants to ...

CLARISSE
(in a heavy French accent)
But I bring you a war relic that my
forefathers claimed in battle against
the fierce Apache nation.

Clarisse kicks away a snake that has slithered near her leg.

BART

What type of war relic?

CLARISSE

An Apache arrowhead, chipped from
the Shoshanti Death Stone.

BART
(mumbling to himself)
Shoshanti Death Stone ...

BART

Okay, come on up.

Sitting inside the treehouse, Bart examines the stone.

BART

Wow, it's incredible!

CLARISSE

I knew you would like it.

BART

Can I have it?

CLARISSE

Of course, Bart. I brought it especially for you.
But first, there are a few things you must do.

CHANGE TO: BART'S TREEHOUSE - CONTINUOUS

Bart dances around in a circle with a grocery bag over his
head.

BART

The Death Stone, hey, hey, hey.
Gonna kill you, yeah, yeah, yeah.

BART

Do I have to wear this stupid bag over my head?

The Fruit

CLARISSE
Yes, it represents the Hood of Shame and
is part of the ritual transfer of the Death
Stone. You are dancing for those the
Stone has already killed.

BART
Eeeh. All right, but there better not be
anything else I have to do for this.

CLARISSE
There is one more thing, Bart. The Death
Stone is very powerful. If passed incorrectly,
it can mean instant death.

MILLHOUSE
Are you sure about this Bart?

BART
Quiet, Millhouse. What do I have to do?

CLARISSE
In passing the Death Stone, we must share the
Breath of Life.

BART
The what?

CLARISSE
We must kiss one time on the lips.

BART
That's it, man — I'm out of here.

MILLHOUSE
I'll do it if he won't.

CLARISSE
(grabs the arrow)
Well, I guess you're not yet worthy of
the Shoshanti Death Stone after all.
Good day, Bart Simpson!

BART

Wait! Maybe I was a bit hasty.

BART

(to himself)
Okay, do I let her go, giving up the
Shoshanti Death Stone forever, or do I keep
the Shoshanti Death Stone and live with this
crippling humiliation for the rest of my
unspectacular, anonymous, pathetic life?

BART

Oh, what the heck. I'll do it.

MILLHOUSE

Pucker up, Bart!

CLARISSE

(dismisses Millhouse)
Leave us, child. The art of love is something
to be practiced in private.

BART

Love! That's it. Make way, Millhouse,
I'm coming through!

CLARISSE

Be still, Bart. If you leave now, you will never
have the Death Stone.

The screen goes black. All we hear is "SMMOOOCH!"

We showed the script to our agent friend. He said,
"Well, it's good for a first effort."

"What do you mean 'first effort?'" we said. "It's pretty
funny, don't you think?"

"Yeah, it's not bad. Some of the characterizations are a
little off. You guys can't expect to be great at this
overnight. Like I said, it's pretty good for a first effort."

We, of course, felt differently, that it was a lot better

than a "first effort." Nonetheless, we decided to move on to more meaningful endeavors. Where was the value to society, we reasoned, contributing to sitcom television? Enough writers were pickling the minds of otherwise intelligent human beings. We wanted to write something real, something of purpose, something that beckoned inspired minds to probe further into their subconscious, taste the bitter/beautiful in life and emerge better off for their journey.

While in the Philippines, Jay became fascinated with the socio-economic factors driving the culture. The poorest people living in cardboard boxes along the Pasig River in Manila. The rich, living in large security compounds in Makati with summer homes in Baguio and Tagaytay. The influence of the United States on the country's development.

The writing of Graham Greene inspired him further. After reading Greene's book, *The Quiet American*, he came up with the idea for the story of Arthur Finch, a fictional former U.S. Secretary of Defense overwhelmed by the burdens of his legacy in office. Called back to the Philippines for the closing ceremonies of Clark Airforce Base and the U.S. Naval Base at Subic Bay, Finch falls in love with a local prostitute. He is obsessed with the notion that by saving this young woman, he can somehow save himself and make reparations for the Asian countries/cultures/people his policies afflicted and the American soldiers that died on their shores.

Finch was based on John McNamara, former secretary of defense under John F. Kennedy and later Lyndon B. Johnson. Jay loved the story, because he wondered what it would be like to feel responsible for the Vietnam war. He dated a prostitute himself while overseas and related to Finch's arrogance/naiveté in believing he could save a girl so destitute from poverty that her own parents sent her to the city to earn money turning tricks. And like me, Jay was intrigued by the notion of the fallen hero, something we talked about a lot. What was it like to be but a shadow of your former self?

Jay understood the story, the politics. In fact, I was amazed two years later when McNamara wrote a book seeking the type of redemption Finch sought. Went on national television, cried on popular late night talk shows. He wanted everyone to know he believed at the time he made the right decisions given the context of the Cold War; yet had he the ability to go back, he would have done things differently. Problem is, you can never go back. For twenty years he lived with the torment of his failed policies in office, looking for a little forgiveness, not from the public, but from himself.

I think Jay saw that same torment in my life, just as I saw it in Finch. Jay ran away to Asia to chase the torment himself, to see the wilderness: the Cambodian death camps; children with limbs blown off by land mines; poverty, squalor, illiteracy. He formed a volleyball team in the refugee camp where he worked. Coached the refugees to play the game he loved so much growing up — a game that brought happiness to their lives, too.

When he got back, he wanted to write about his experience in Asia. Finch became his vehicle, and for a while it was mine too, lending my own experience to the development of Finch's character. We spent our afternoons writing in the waning summer heat, because sometimes it can continue to wane here in southern California clear through November — clickety-clack on the keyboard. But Jay moved back east to spend time with his father in Washington, DC. He hated Los Angeles. Felt like he was withering away in a plastic town, after the realism he experienced in the jungles of Asia.

When he left, I continued to write the screenplay myself, even though I had never been to the Philippines. I depended on Jay for his descriptions of the landscape; his recall of the villages and provinces he visited while living there; the life he infused in every street scene, describing sidewalk vendors, market gardens, and the view from the bluffs overlooking Taal Lake.

So, I went to the store and bought a series of travel books that combined pictures with regional maps, some history and a few stories thrown in for good measure. I used the books to gain a feel for the culture, the lifestyle — snapshots of fishermen unloading their nets, jeepneys plying the streets of Manila. Using the travel books, I guided Finch through the Philippine countryside, fleeing a life he could no longer bear.

Finch's journey became my own as he drove out of the city, following the mapped roadways up through Tagaytay and down to Batangas. He watched the sun set and snorkeled in the China Sea. He chased sand crabs on a deserted beach and did things I wished I could do, while sitting cooped up in my room. My imagination ran wild all over my keyboard, staring at the screen watching the scene unfold through my fingers — birds flying far across the corners of my mind.

*C*hapter 22

It amazes me sometimes to hear what the body can endure — the freezing cold, people freezing past any reasonable point of return, yet many have returned; the scalding heat, hours without air, days without water, weeks without food, months of contagion, years of contamination; not to mention amputation, mutilation. A limb may be missing, where only a scar remains, but the body adapts. The person lives, functions, feeds and grooms, using just feet to drive, or a mouth to propel a wheel chair along a busy street. Some of these incredible feats are due in part to scientific invention, but most are the result of sheer human will and determination.

Yet, there's nothing admirable about suffering, just as there is no shame in comfort. My dad's girlfriend was a psychologist. Over the phone, we had talked about the benefits psychotropic drugs were having on her patients, drugs like Prozac and Zoloft. People who one week wandered under a dark cloud of discontent, found themselves the next week living their lives complete. I wondered if these drugs might help me.

I read a few books on depression, books like *Listening to Prozac* and *You Mean I Don't Have to Feel This Way?* The more I read, the more I realized clinical depression seemed to mirror the fatigue I suffered. Cycles were similar — up one week, down the next — like being trapped in a glass elevator that never stops and has no doors, so you can never get out. Many of my symptoms even mirrored those experienced by people with depression — fatigue, phantom pains, cloudy thinking, troubled sleep, fear of the outside, and fear I might never get better.

I concluded that where clinical depression is a depression of the mind, chronic fatigue syndrome is a depression of the body. Some doctors believe it too, that the same chemical imbalances that cause depression can cause chronic fatigue. They believe that all one must do to treat the illness is alter the chemical imbalance which is depressing the body's immune system at the cellular level.

I made an appointment with Megan — the doctor I had been consulting. Told her about my desire to try one of these new anti-depressants, said to be "clean drugs" with few side effects. But Megan said she wouldn't support it. Said that they screw with your mind. The fact I knew she was a Scientologist and that psychotropic drugs were against her basic beliefs led me to seek a second opinion from another doctor I frequented (like shopping for automobiles — if one dealer doesn't have the car, find a dealer that does).

Murray Susser, a supposed expert in the field of chronic fatigue syndrome, had run about a million tests on me; tried about a thousand vitamin combinations, all of which did nothing for me — or made me sicker. Said he didn't recommend anti-depressants; said that they may help, but they may also make me worse:

"I can see that if I don't let you try them, you'll keep seeing other doctors until you find someone that isn't familiar with your history who will," he said to me at last. "Now, I'm against this, but in certain situations anti-depressants have been known to work. Nothing we've tried has worked with you so far, so I'm going to give you a prescription for Prozac. Take it for a month and we'll see what happens."

"That's what I want to do. Let's see what happens."

At least we understood each other. He must have seen the determination/desperation in my eyes as I stared at him from across the desk. I walked out of his office with a smile on my face, hope in my gait and the prescription I wanted clutched in my hand.

Once I bought the medicine, it took me a while to pop my first pill — my little yellow dose. I was afraid, unsure. I heard some amazing things about psychotropic drugs, but a few horror stories as well — people deteriorating into panic attacks, going ballistic, killing family members. Most of the literature claimed such stories were false, but who knew what drugs like this could do — drugs strong enough to alter your mind, make wonderful a miserable life? Could they make miserable a not so wonderful life?

Called my friend Nick in New York.

"Did you get it?" he said.

"Yeah, I did. I think I'm afraid to take it, though."

"Why?"

"What if it makes me worse?"

"It's not going to make you worse. You've just got to try it. If you start to feel a bit funny, stop taking it."

Nick had been taking Prozac a little over two months. A chronic fatigue sufferer like myself, he experienced significantly more energy. He started performing again with his rock band, doing late night shows, taking his music on the road.

"Sometimes I wonder if there really is such a thing as chronic fatigue," he said. "What does that mean? I'm starting to think that it's all in my mind, that I start thinking my body is tired and depressed and I end up feeling shitty. With anti-depressants I don't feel that way. I feel energized, alive, healthy, 'normal.'"

"Really," I said.

"Really."

So, I called up my dad's girlfriend.

"But, what if it makes me worse?"

"Prozac doesn't work like that. It merely corrects the imbalance of serotonin to the brain. If there's no imbalance, it doesn't do anything. Basically, the worst thing that can happen is it won't have any effect on you at all."

Still concerned over consequences, I pondered taking the drug for several days. Virtually everything I took caused some degree of negative reaction within my body. Prozac, in my opinion, was a fairly serious drug. If vitamin C could send my body reeling, I wondered what a negative reaction to Prozac might do.

I consulted my *I Ching Workbook*. The *I Ching Workbook* had become my oracle during times of trial. Consulting it wouldn't necessarily change my course of action, but it might make me think about something. It always gave me an interesting perspective on the question at hand, because its response when consulted was always open to interpretation.

I grabbed the same three pennies I always used to construct the *I Ching* hexagrams, which represent the coming together of heaven and earth and are the key to the oracle. I sat down in a comfortable corner of my room and focused on my query, "What will be the outcome of my taking Prozac?" I let the pennies fall — *BENEFIT* read the first hexagram:

> Exceptional energy is being drawn into the current situation. Many things will become possible, even very difficult undertakings. Pursue your goals on a daily basis and remain persevering.

Which made me think, "This is it! This new medication will benefit my health. I'll get better and better, maybe in a matter of weeks, days, hours." I could feel my heart pump, as if destiny was upon me. I realize it's strange to get excited over such things, yet my entire life revolved around the resolution of my illness.

When consulting the *I Ching,* the first hexagram (of which there are a total of sixty-four) tends to represent the current situation — the mindset of the one who queries. Changing lines within the first hexagram (which, depending on how the pennies fall, may or may not occur) send you to the final hexagram, which tends to represent the outcome of the query. Changing lines in my query sent me to the second to last hexagram in the book — *AFTER THE END*. It read:

> A state of perfect equilibrium has been reached. Everything seems to be in the best of order. The

situation represents a familiar historical pattern: after a civilization's exhilarating climb to its glorious peak, decline begins ... You cannot avoid the decline that comes AFTER THE END, yet you can learn to survive such times and emerge strengthened in spirit and character. Above all, do not try to maintain the illusion of the ideal that exists now ... if anything can possibly go wrong, it will.

And I thought, "Great. I'm screwed. Doesn't look good, but what can it possibly mean? What exhilarating climb? What glorious peak? I've been in a valley so wide, I feel like I'm entrenched at bottom of the Grand Canyon."

"Perhaps the perfect state of equilibrium will be my outcome; 'the best of order', my result. For a while, I'll feel complacent and comfortable, which is exactly how I'd like to feel."

I was confused, bemused, perplexed. But, I didn't care; I was resolved. I popped my first pill that night and woke up feeling nothing ... or maybe just a little burst of energy. I continued to take it throughout the day, then the next day, and the next.

Day five on Prozac I was sailing, but it wasn't a comfortable feeling. It wasn't the kind that took me away, carried me, so soon I would be free.

It felt like caffeine, like a jolt of nervous energy coursing though my veins. Just as I started to feel tired, that loving burst would kick in, clear the clouds from my mind and leave me wired, looking for things to do, places to go, errands to run, run, run.

I was like a time bomb, or some coke addict, nervously gnashing my teeth. An old friend's sister was driving through the neighborhood and saw me crossing the street.

"Mark, how are you?"

"I'm doing all right. I've been sick, but I'm starting to feel better."

"We're having a Christmas party tonight. Why don't you come?"

"Sounds cool, thanks. If I'm up to it, maybe I'll stop by."

The Fruit

Got home after a long walk and did some writing. As the day edged on, my energy did too. I ate some dinner, showered and dressed, then jumped into my car and drove the five or so blocks to my friend Tina's house for my first Christmas party in three years.

I felt nervous as I approached the front door and shivered a little as I rang the door bell. I even felt a little faint as Tina came to the door and I stepped into a swarm of faces, staring back at me to see if I might be someone they recognized. I wasn't. So, they went on laughing and talking. Tina took me by the arm and led me into the dining room amongst the younger crowd and faces I recognized.

"Mark — Hey — How's it going?"

"All right. And yourself?"

"Can't believe how long your hair is. What's been up?"

"Not much really ... I've been real sick, but I'm starting to feel better. I've been doing some writing."

"Oh yeah, what kind?"

"Poetry and music. Right now, I'm working on a screenplay."

"Had anything published?"

"A couple poems, that's about it. It's not easy to get published. I'm trying to see where I can go with this screenplay I'm writing. What have you been doing?"

"I've got my own business. I'm teamed up with a couple guys and we're trying to sell a few animation projects."

"Movie animation."

"No, cartoons actually."

"Sounds pretty fun."

"Yeah. We've been working at it for some time now. I'm thinking about selling my share of the business and starting something else."

"How come?"

"Well, I would still be involved with the company, because I have most of the connections in the industry. I'm just ready to start working on another project."

"I see."

"Listen, I've got this friend who's a producer. Give me a call next week and I'll give you his number. He's looking for ideas all the time. You guys could have lunch, see what happens."

"Okay, I'll do that."

We said our good-byes. Or at least nodded with mutual understanding that our discussion came to a close and that we were moving on to talk to other guests at the party.

As the evening drew on, I felt more comfortable, conversations came easier. I shared stories with people I knew; met and shared stories with people I didn't know; circled the room and sampled Christmas goodies set out on silver and glass trays.

"Have some of this."

"Try some of that."

"Would you like some wine?"

"No thanks, I'm fine."

I left later that night smiling, ebullient. Made more promises to call people I talked with. I walked the rain-soaked path back to my car with a spring in my step. So much energy, I felt so alive in contrast to the evening mist that seemed like a rich cotton blanket, bedding the empty streets down to sleep.

Back at my house, I brushed my teeth and climbed into bed, tired, but restless and filled with angst. Tried reading for a while to calm myself down, which worked — sort of. So, I shut off the light, closed my eyes and tried sleeping.

Flitter, flutter. Two hours later, I realized I was still awake, my body shifting, searching for the comfortable position I couldn't find. My muscles tense, I found myself clawing the sheet. Pitter, patter. My heart felt like it was pounding out of my chest; my breath shallow, as if I were hyperventilating. No doubt about it, I was having a full-blown anxiety attack.

I ran down to Dave's room, "Dave man, wake up. Dave, wake up!"

"What is it?"

"My heart feels like it's beating a thousand times a minute. It's the Prozac I've been taking, I think I'm flipping out."

"What time is it?"

"It's 2:00 a.m."

192

"Why don't you call the hospital? If you need to go, I'll take you down there."

"All right. I keep thinking about River Phoenix. That guy wigged out and died."

"Mark, you're not going to die. He was on heroin, speed, alcohol and who knows what else. Just call the hospital so we can get some sleep."

I called the local emergency room. The nurse on duty told me she couldn't really help me and that I'd have to come in. But it was 2:00 a.m., cold outside and I didn't feel like going in. I called Dr. Susser:

"Mark, sounds like you're just having a panic attack. You're going to be okay. Stop taking the medication tomorrow and try to get some sleep tonight. If you absolutely can't sleep, then head down to the emergency room. They can give you a shot to help you calm down and sleep. All right?"

"All right."

Meanwhile I was freezing, freaked out. I climbed into bed with Dave, who wasn't too happy about it. After calming me down a bit, he left me to go sleep up in my bed.

Next day, I apologized to Dave for taking over his bed. I stopped taking the Prozac, too, but it didn't seem to matter. The Prozac triggered something in me — a reaction deep within my cells.

The next night I had another anxiety attack, during which I went down and crawled into Dave's bed again. Dave, a quintessential homophobe, stayed with me for about fifteen minutes, then walked up to catch some sleep in my bed.

After the second night, I stopped sleeping in Dave's bed and simply learned to accept the anxiety attack that came each night at about 2:00 a.m. Braced myself for it, like the werewolf in London, transforming under a pale bitter moon.

"You're off the medication?" Dr. Susser asked.

"Yes."

"How long have you been off it?"

"Three weeks."

"And you're still having these attacks each night."

"That's right."

"That's impossible. The medication has been out of your system for several days now."

"Maybe it has, but I'm still having the same reaction."

"It's got to be something else."

"I don't think so."

Amazing how sensitive my body. As a result of my anxiety attacks I consulted a psychiatrist, who frequently prescribed psychotropic medications for his patients.

"You're having anxiety attacks from medication you took for ten days and stopped taking over a month ago?"

"That's right."

"That's impossible!"

"Look, I've been sick four years. I've been to doctors in the United States, Mexico and Canada. None have been able to successfully treat me. No one really has a clue as to what's wrong with me. At this point in my illness, I can assure you, nothing is *impossible.*"

So, he gave me some Xanax to calm me down, help me sleep, keep me from having my anxiety attacks. I was like those people who take uppers to start the day and downers to end it (sometimes literally); "clinically-medicated drug addicts," I suppose the proper term might be; cabinets full of pills in little brown childproof bottles, the letters "Rx" and a phone number at the bottom, to make it easy to dial your trip. Yeah, anyway ...

The Xanax left me tired, spaced out. I stopped taking it two days later, so he switched me to Zoloft. Said it was a better drug than Prozac. Said it was newer, with less side effects, an all-around "sleeker" drug. Said he never would have prescribed Prozac for me the way my doctor did. It all sounded good and I believed him.

Sitting in my living room, I'm holding onto my practitioner samples of Zoloft, which the psychiatrist gave me so I wouldn't have to pay for it out of my pocket, on my limited budget. I'm thinking I've got the Cadillac of anti-depressants, the magic pill. If this one won't do it, nothing will.

Before I take it, I quickly consult my *I Ching Workbook.* I toss my pennies and build my hexagrams. This is the big one, the fat one, the question that really matters — "If I

194

take this medication, what will be the outcome?"

I asked it this way, because you can't ask yes/no questions. Nothing is that defined. Answers are never black or white, but shades of grey, which I remember hearing somewhere. I think it was a made-for-TV movie, but I could have heard it before that, I just can't recall. My starting point: hexagram forty-seven — *ADVERSITY*. It read:

> This time of difficulty is a natural turn of events. It will present real problems, but they can be endured with the proper attitude. They may even lead exceptional persons into success ... remain emotionally stable and optimistic ... ADVERSITY has been brought about by fate.

This made sense to me. My situation could not have been described better — I was faced with severe adversity, determined to get through it.

Changing lines in my query sent me to the last hexagram in the book: hexagram sixty-four — *BEFORE THE END*. This seemed strange because my sense of logical progression told me *AFTER THE END* (hexagram sixty-three) should come after *BEFORE THE END*, with *THE END* falling somewhere in the middle.

It doesn't. When I read it, I understood why. At the same time, I understood why the eastern mindset often clashes with the western. In the west, all focus is on the outcome, the completion of an act — winning the race, winning the game, seeing your portrait plastered on a wall. It's not about getting there, it's all about being there, being seen being there. Everyone wants to touch you because you're there. Then you die and you're in heaven, perched on cloud nine, plucking strings and drinking wine, with every other proud bastard who prayed his way into God's green wonderful?

That's it. There you perch, bones and flesh buried in earth, or scattered as ashes over a shivering sea. Kind of makes you wonder, what the fuck do you do up there for ten billion years? Sit and be happy? Sit and feel loved? How many people do you talk to who can sit for ten minutes, let alone an eternity? Will their spirits act any

195

differently? Sort of makes you wonder. Most people I know would be better off in hell. At least there's action down there. And you can bet they get the six o'clock evening news — blood, guts, and fear in surround sound on a forty-foot screen.

Getting back to my point. In the east, everything is ongoing. They're still living amongst the spirits of their ancestors, seeking counsel when needed. Reincarnation brings grandfathers and grandmothers, brothers and sisters back into the fray amongst the living. Eternity isn't up there in heaven, it's right here on earth, where everything is in the process of becoming. No one is trying to squeeze everything into one lifetime. They're merely students on a journey, living and learning what they can, until finally, after about a thousand, million lifetimes they don't have to come back again. They will have merged and become one with the universe.

Hexagram sixty-four — *BEFORE THE END* — it read:

The accomplishment of a goal is in sight. At the time BEFORE THE END there is great promise for the future ... The coming situation will be strange to you in every way, unlike any that you have experienced ... for in many ways the time will be nothing short of rebirth.

And I knew I was onto something. I could feel it and started counting the days until I'd be better. A nervous feeling came over me. What would I do if I felt better tomorrow -- completely better, cured? Would I look for a job? Take a trip? Been down so long, forgot what it was like to be up and alive, doing the town. Where would I start? How would I go about starting over? I was acting like someone who purchases a Lotto ticket and starts counting the money before the numbers roll in; starts carving their place among America's elite fortunes:

"The first thing I'll do is buy a house for cousin Vinny, 'cause Vinny's been like a brother to me and he's such a great guy, he deserves it." Everyone likes to think they're Jane/John generous, when they're really thinking about that new Porsche, that new house overlooking the lake they visited on their last vacation, the trip they've been wanting to take but have been putting it off and putting it off, because they didn't have enough money or time — working for dollars, earning a dime.

I stopped taking Zoloft seven days after I started. It made my head swim. It left me spaced out, feeling like I was high on drugs, because I was. I floated through the day, all sounds muffled, hushed. I couldn't focus, felt confused, but felt alright about feeling confused, because the quietude made my world seem dreamlike and peaceful.

"Why did you stop taking Zoloft?" my psychiatrist said.

"It made me feel spaced out."

"That may have been merely a temporary reaction to the medication. It takes awhile to start working. Sometimes two to three weeks, sometimes a month, occasionally longer."

But who's got time to wait and see if something bad is going to get worse? After taking the Zoloft, I was basically bedridden about a week. Had I taken it longer, my experience told me I would have been bedridden longer still. Even after I stopped taking it, the spaced out sensation I experienced didn't go away. It lingered the way everything seemed to linger: the days, my frustrations; the months, my illness; the years, my life.

Another treatment tried and failed ... guess I had to know for sure. Now that I knew, I sat down, leaned back, closed my eyes and wondered, just like we all sometimes wonder: What now?

Part 4:

Rebirth

Chapter 23

My recovery started around Christmas time.
Another Christmas that came and went. Another New
Year's. Another year I watched from the sideline as the
Harvard Christmas rugby game was played and won/lost.
I can't remember who won that year, whether it was the
old boys, or the slightly "younger" boys, because there
were no young boys playing the Harvard Christmas rugby
game any more. The boys were now grown — the boyz
were all men.

Around this time two Alexes stumbled back into my
life. The first Alex was my old girlfriend, the family
friend who disappeared six months before. She called me
up the week after I stopped taking Zoloft and I was still
feeling a little dazed and confused from the experience.

"Hi, Mark. It's Alex."

A bit nervous, I replied, "Alex, how's it going?
I haven't heard from you in a while. How've you been?"

"Well, good and bad. I'm in town, staying with a
friend. I was wondering if you would like to meet for
coffee while I'm here?"

"Actually, I haven't been feeling that well lately. Well
actually I have, but I'm not feeling that great right now.
Would you mind coming over here?"

"Okay, but I don't have transportation. I'm out in
Alhambra. If I take a cab over, can you drive me back?"

"Sure, I could do that."

I watched from my living room window as her blue

and yellow cab pulled up to the curb the afternoon of the next day. I straightened up a bit before she arrived, but not too much. I was trying to conserve my energy.

On the phone Alex talked about how terrible she looked; how terribly tired she felt, going through the divorce with her ex-husband, fighting him all the way. Married a little over two years with limited assets to divide up, Alex was trying to recoup what she felt was rightfully hers. At the same time, he was trying to keep what he felt was rightfully his. Like the War of the Roses, their battle deteriorated into a nasty mess — accusations and name-calling, jab here, stab there. That third-grade mentality adults regress to when they're trying to hurt each other.

But she didn't look tired, or terrible. Her infectious smile was warm, her face beautiful. Her hug hello erased the distance between us, and I was glad to see her.

We talked as we sat on my living room couch, filling in the months since we last spoke. No longer able to support herself, Alex moved home to live with her family in Texas. She spent most of her day in bed depressed, afraid of the world outside, afraid of its demons, hiding from its lions and tigers and bears. For her, the world had become an ugly place where only bad things happened.

"I try to be positive. I'll have a couple good days of feeling, if not happy, at least somewhat safe, or at peace. Then something happens, a flat tire, another credit company demanding money for a bill I thought I paid a long time ago. The littlest thing sends me into a tailspin that takes days to recover from."

"Can't you just recognize it for what it is? Everybody's had a flat tire at least once in their life. Sometimes bills don't get paid on time, or the credit card company makes a mistake. It sounds to me like you're having a problem putting these incidents into perspective."

"That's exactly it and I don't know what to do about it. I feel overwhelmed all the time and a lot of it has to do with the fact that I can't seem to find a medication that works for me. Things that used to just bounce right off, become major issues in my life."

We talked about her life for a while, then started

talking about mine; my recent experience/complications with anti-depressants. We talked about the screenplay I was writing and my new roommate. She asked me if I'd been dating.

"You know, I haven't dated since we stopped seeing each other."

"Really," she said.

"Not that I worry about it too much. I've been pretty busy and things have been going well for me, in terms of developing new friendships and finding some direction in my life."

"That's good."

"It's good and bad."

We talked about the way things ended between us. The last time she came through Los Angeles.

"You know, I never thought I'd hear from you again," I said.

"Why would you think that?" she asked. "I never planned to lose contact with you."

"It just seemed that way, like girlfriends I've had in the past. When it's over, it's usually over. I don't even talk to most of my old girlfriends, so I figured I probably wouldn't be talking to you, either."

Two lonely people, too lonely in our worlds. At first I sat, my arm around my rediscovered friend. Later, I lounged, my arms wrapped around my deep and closest friend, our bodies warm and close, growing warmer, moving closer. Lying down, side-by-side, our conversation softened to a whisper.

"Can I kiss you?" I asked.

"Only if it's something more than physical, and only if you mean it," she replied. "I don't want to get hurt."

"Neither do I."

We kissed and cuddled for a long time on the couch; made our way up to my room; under the covers of my bed, naked and intimate.

The earth shook at four o'clock that morning. The jolt tossed Alex into mid-air screaming, which in turn woke me up. The lights in the city below were dark. No power in our neighborhood, or many others for that matter.

"Mark, what's happening?"

"I don't know. Are you all right? It felt like an earthquake." Freaked-out, we huddled for a moment waiting for the tremors to stop, before checking the house for things broken, hanging, dangerous. Hysterical radio broadcasters reported on the worst quake to hit Los Angeles in years.

"Yeahh baby!" my roommate screamed from downstairs. "Did you feel that? That was awesome! We're rockin' now!"

Alex hysterical, Dave on fire, wishing the power would come back on so he could blast his head-banger music and scream a little louder, I scrambled to find a flashlight, calming Alex down, telling Dave to "mellow out" because Alex was hysterical, only to discover the flashlight I had didn't work.

"Mark, what are we going to do?" Alex said. "Is it safe? Should we go outside? What happens if another one comes? What if the house collapses? You know I've heard that during earthquakes ..."

"The house is not going to collapse. Just stay here, I'm going to look around a little to shut off the gas and to make sure nothing's broken." I flashed back to the L.A. riots, the city looted and burning. Rioters could have a field day now, if they weren't too busy running for cover.

"We're rockin' baby!" Dave shouted again and again.

Aftershocks continued all night, the next day, and for several months thereafter. I experienced the San Francisco quake of '89. Itchy. Anxious. Unstable fault lines, following me all over the place, like an irascible shadow — like I was "Bad Luck" Shleprock, riding the whip of a dragon's tail over a long streak of natural disasters.

In Los Angeles, it seemed like we had major earthquakes daily for about two months. "Another earthquake, magnitude 5.3 rocked the southland today," went the frequent story on the evening news. First it was fires, then floods, now earthquakes. Living with disaster was becoming a way of life. Wrong year to say to your wife, "Hey honey, what do you say we pack up and move to Los Angeles. The weather's beautiful. We can buy a house, settle down. What do you say?" Great timing, friend!

Alex and I agreed not to expect too much — no full-blown love affair that would be the answer to all our problems. Instead, we sought merely to stay in touch, stay close, see each other when we could, and talk to each other when we needed support.

She called me from the plane. Said she had been crying. Someone thought they recognized her as the star of a popular afternoon soap — *Days of Our Lives, As the World Turns* — one of those. She had had a couple drinks ... the reception faded in, faded out.

"Mark, I had such a good time the past two days. It was such a wonderful escape from life. Now I'm going back, I don't know what I'm going to do, or when I'll see you again."

"I know. We'll just do the best we can, and then see what happens. Okay?"

"Okay."

"Are you going to be alright?"

"I don't know."

"I'll talk to you soon."

"Okay."

In helping someone else, sometimes you find strength you never thought you had. Driving home from the airport that day, my energy improved dramatically from the day Alex called. My tailspin into exhaustion reversed itself to an upswing. I felt as if I could accomplish anything.

Driving home, I had a vision of what it would be like to be free of illness, what it would feel like to have a stable life. In my mind I could see myself comfortable, confident. I pressed the accelerator as I descended the Baldwin Hills, headed north on La Brea and back towards my home in Los Feliz. Hands tight on the wheel, wheels sailing over asphalt, in a dreamlike state, I felt I was flying.

with dark clouds over the valley
the black hat marauder descends
into the dusk
       to take the town, to take the town

Dazed And Fatigued

green hills flourish to the east
and to the west
no wind but the air is clear
the air is fresh
and the man who shed his shadow
has come to take the town

he walks alone, but is not lonely
he knows fear, but is no longer afraid
as darkness clouds over the valley
the black hat marauder descends

      to claim the town, to claim the town

the town that does not know

      it belongs to him.

*C*hapter 24

The second Alex stumbled back into my life via my roommate Dave. We all went to high school together — Dave, Al and I. While Dave and Al were close friends and had remained close, Al and I were what I would call party friends growing up. The only time we ever saw each other, or spent time together was in pursuit of or just subsequent to the consumption of large quantities of alcohol and/or drugs. Sometimes we were looking for girls, but usually, at that young age, our primary concern was getting as drunk and high as possible. A car/room full of teenage boys all shouting and screaming, emotions careening, "Suck it up! Suck it down! Hey dude, pass the bong so I can cannonball!"

We hadn't actually stayed in touch as he went off to San Diego State University and I headed up to Berkeley, but I sometimes heard reports through Dave of Al's wild escapades — nudie bars and 502s, a couple overnight stints in Mexican *jaliscos.* Alex lived his life on the wilder side of wild, often calling on friends and family to discretely bail him out of situations gone sticky and foul.

Drinking was Al's biggest problem, which made him erratic; one minute, he was dependable fun, the next a jail sentence waiting to happen — midnight brawls, drunken crawls through bars up and down the California coast.

When he wasn't drinking, Al was a man in search of himself. He sat in on inspirational seminars, and was open to new and alternative ideas. Al had a huge heart and was the kind of guy you could trust, if you didn't know you

207

couldn't trust him.

He called to talk to Dave two, three, even four times a day. Sometimes he called so often, Dave would say, "If that's Al, tell him I'm not here."

On the days Dave wasn't around, Al and I sometimes talked. He knew about my illness and often asked questions about it. Just as I knew about his illness — his alcoholism — which I often asked questions about. Asked him why he was such a destructive force in his own life. Didn't he care about himself? Didn't he care enough about himself to care about the people he loved, and the people he hurt?

Al did care. He always called to share ideas and information he heard about treatments supposedly curing people like me from illnesses like chronic fatigue.

One day Al called me up, ring-a-ring-dang, as the phone shook and sang. "Hey," he said, which was how he started all his conversations and was insulted if you asked, "Who is this?" because he expected you to know. So, he never gave his name. He'd continue to say, "Hey," until you realized it was him and said, "What's up, Al?"

"My girlfriend's roommate, who is so hot, by the way, just told me about this Korean doctor she's seeing. Supposedly he's incredible."

"What does he treat with," I asked, "Chinese herbs, acupuncture? I've had some problems with those types of treatments in the past."

"No, it's nothing like that. He does something called acupressure that aligns your body so it can heal itself."

"Yeah, I know what acupressure is."

"He can treat virtually everything. My girlfriend's going to see him to see if it can improve her asthma. He's already treated my girlfriend's roommate for some spinal problems, and her roommate's mom for a long-term illness. The mom flies out from Colorado every week just to see him. Why don't you give him a call?"

"Well, maybe I will. Are you sure there's no herbs or remedies I have to take?"

"I'm pretty sure. Let me call my girlfriend. I'll ask her and get his number for you."

"All right. Then call me back."

Dr. Lee didn't use needles. He didn't believe in medicine. His work was based solely on the flow of *chi* or energy, through the body. It focused on the premise that as we progress through life, stress or injury-related blockages occur, stifling the flow of chi, which leads to sickness and disease. By loosening the blocks, thus restoring the body to its natural balance, the body is free to cure itself.

The first day I went to the treatment center, I witnessed a woman crippled with multiple sclerosis for fifteen years take her first steps — legs trembling, arms assisting her steps, but steps just the same. Only thing I can say is, at that moment, with that lead-in, I felt a tremendous amount of hope.

Dr. Lee sat in lotus position, legs crossed into his lap as I entered his treatment room. His assistant, who also served as translator, asked me to lay face up on the cushioned mat next to Dr. Lee. The room was cold. I didn't know what I was in for. In broken English, Dr. Lee asked me to take deep breaths and "*relaxe.*"

The deciding factor in my visit to see Dr. Lee was his diagnostic method. On your first visit, he told you through his interpreter not only what was wrong, but how many treatments it would take to correct the problem.

For twenty minutes, he cracked and manipulated my body in ways I never previously experienced or imagined possible. He popped my hip, spine, and neck. Pop. Crack. Literally pounded on my backside. Thump-pound. Thump. Dug his fingers into sensitive pressure points on my face, hands, back, legs, and feet. Crack. Crack-pop-crack. It was so painful, I laughed hysterically, uncontrollably. When I finally stood, weary from the shock and pain, Dr. Lee told me it would take eleven treatments to "cure" my problem.

"What do you mean by cure? Do you mean that after eleven treatments, I'll be completely better?"

"It's different for different people," his assistant answered. "I've seen some people with illnesses like yours start to improve dramatically after the second or third treatment. Others, it takes longer. Patients Dr. Lee says he can help, generally feel much better after the treatments."

I paid fifty bucks for the treatment, feeling almost guilty, like I hadn't paid enough. Walking out, I thought to myself, "He essentially re-aligned my entire body, promised I would be cured after eleven treatments and in return I gave him just fifty bucks." Seemed such a small price for so much, but would it work? With the bright sun on the sidewalk reflecting heat and light, I climbed into my car and drove off completely blown away.

They asked me to return for treatments daily to keep the chi energy coursing through my body during this critical time. Dr. Lee's office was across town. Didn't feel like making the drive there and back every day. Not to mention, after my appointments my body was so beat up, I didn't feel much like driving. So, I took the opportunity to spend time with old friends who lived near Dr. Lee's office. I even met a new one.

Jana had been a chronic fatigue sufferer like myself for several years. Came down with the flu one day, and like stars in the sky, never really went away. Jana was a friend of a friend of a close friend of mine and we met over the phone, like I met my other fatigued friends Tamara and Nick.

We had spoken only twice, when I called and asked if I could crash at her place for a couple days. Bold, eh? Felt a little strange asking, but Jana seemed pretty understanding, and lived only a few blocks from Dr. Lee's office. When I explained my situation, she said, "Sure."

I packed my bags and drove out to her rent-controlled Santa Monica apartment. City controls the rent and the landlords control the apartments, swapped like commodities on a black market supported by finder's fees and false assurances. I felt awkward meeting Jana at first. We were two people who never really met and yet, here I was spending a couple nights on her floor. The awkwardness ended quickly, as we sat down and started talking.

We shared war stories, so to speak, as her new kitten Kayla scratched, climbed and made fodder of Jana's living room couch, chairs, and tables — a monstrously cute gremlin with paws, claws and a fuzzy-wuzzy tail.

I loved getting out of the house. Even one day away from home was like a vacation for me. Jana had a BIG SCREEN TV with cable and a remote control. At home, I couldn't feel good about myself watching television all day. Half of me would lurch out from my body, stare down and scold the other half — disappointed, finger shaking, brow furrowing, "You're not going to just lay there and do nothing but watch TV all day, are you?!"

While on vacation, or spending time with friends, I was officially "doing" something, so everything immediately became okay. I allowed myself to sleep in, surf the channels, and lounge in the afternoon air. I could *relaxe* and let someone/something else entertain me for a while.

I stayed with Jana a couple days, returned to my house for a night, then spent four days with another friend, and two days with yet another. Each day, Dr. Lee pounded, twisted, corrected, and cured.

I went through a couple days during the treatment, when I could barely move my body. So, I took a day off. "You're experiencing a deep healing," Dr. Lee's assistant told me. "It's best to rest and drink a lot of fluids. You'll feel better tomorrow." Which I did, then returned to complete my treatment — eleven short days to combat the haze. When finished, they assured me my chi was in fact circulating properly.

"That's great, but you know I'm not really feeling cured," I said as I signed my last check for my last payment in return for healing services rendered.

"Well, it may take a while. There's been a lot of damage to your system. It takes a while to rebuild. You didn't expect to get better overnight, did you? Of course not."

"I guess I did. Dr. Lee said I'd be cured once I finished the treatments."

"Well, you are cured in relation to opening the blockages that have hindered your recovery these past few years. It just takes a little time for the rest of your body to catch up."

And there was that little word — "time" — again.

I could hear it tick-tick, ticking away, the time slip-slap, slipping through my fingers like sand through an hourglass. They never want to admit their treatment failed, or wasn't as successful as promised. They try to tell you things are still on track, like a train slow to get going. I'll tell you this, there are no money-back guarantees in medicine, and it doesn't matter if you're talking scientific medicine, or ancient medicine wheels these days. I knew what he was really saying: "Lower your expectations. You'll get better, maybe, I hope, at some inestimable juncture in the not-too-distant future, when rhyme, reason, and reality merge on planes juxtaposed to express eternity." Say what?

Despite my obvious disappointment, my life dramatically changed for the better as a result of Dr. Lee's treatment program. The required daily visits, coupled with layovers at friends houses, inadvertently altered my existence. It forced me to let go my life's tempered crutches — the measured distances I walked, my daily routines. I stopped stretching, stopped meditating, and most of all, stopped fanatisizing, timing my day around a series of scheduled events.

The physical demands of Dr. Lee's treatment required I rest. Yet I couldn't, because it was more convenient for me not to go home, hole up, and bunker down for an afternoon of recuperation, fretting over every obscure ache, pain, energy drain.

Instead, I drove directly to friends houses; friends like Jana, houses without crutches, houses that for me held no routines. I was free falling/flying, which at first scared me.

I quickly realized my fears were unfounded. Seven days on the road, so to speak, and I grew stronger not sicker. If I just took care of myself, remained conscious, but not overly so, of my activity level; if I did the best I could to live my life and enjoy it, I believed and knew I would eventually get better. "Why wait to enjoy life tomorrow," I thought, "when I'm forced to live it today?"

And you're saying, "But isn't that what you were doing all along? Isn't that what everyone suggested you do? To go out there and just do it anyway despite how you felt?" That's not what I'm saying at all. There's a difference between denying your fears, anxiety, physical reality and pushing yourself to be something you are not *versus* coming to terms with your physical/mental reality, accepting yourself for who you are and realize that despite your situation there is no reason to be afraid. More than that, there's no reason you can't find love, happiness, solace in the midst of your trying situation, wherein the realization of that love, happiness, solace, is the remedy by which you will ultimately realize your cure — a cure that does not merely remedy your physical disability, but your mental and psycho-spiritual disabilities as well.

All this is obviously simple to say, harder to live, but live it I did. I started giving myself a break, cutting myself some slack as my entire life/my perspective on life changed. Instead of always worrying about getting better tomorrow, I once again started thinking about ways I could enjoy my life to its fullest today.

*C*hapter 25

Look at the little ants who build cities; the tiny bugs, whose clever minds have enabled them to fly. Watch the cars driving in the streets, propelling them — like bugs in a carriage — certain distances in an hour that might otherwise take a day. These funny vehicles communicate, or rather the bugs communicate with their vehicles. Blink-blink-blink, I'm turning left. Blink-blink-blink, I'm turning right. These modes of transportation are a means of self-expression, signifying frequently not only preferences, but status or social class. Watch how other bugs stare enviously, as a real "nice" mode of transportation passes by. Witness their shame and inadequacy — this other bug must be better than they are. This other bug must be a better bug. Yes, maybe that bug is "special!"

Obscure and bitter little metaphor, but you get my drift. Makes driving in heavy traffic fun instead of frantic, and helps put things into perspective. Anyway, getting back to the turn in my story, the turn in my life. Life turns like a snake, in and out of holes, slithering along, sometimes slower than fast, most times faster than slow.

Alex and I were dating again, trying not to define our relationship, or build too much into it. Neither one of us could support ourselves, nor would we be able to support ourselves for some time at the rate things were going. She lived in Texas, while I lived in southern California. We talked on the phone two to three nights a week, which at times was sad and hard, but it was enough.

I started to think about going back to school. No

longer was I trying to recapture my glory days and the life I lost at Berkeley. Nor did I envision myself walking fancy-free among protesters, peddlers, beggars and musicians on a sun-splashed, breezy afternoon in Sproul Plaza, flowers and trees and students in bloom.

I merely wanted to graduate, get my diploma, and get on with my life. I called in some old AP (advanced placement) credits I earned in high school and decided to take a minor in Rhetoric instead of completing my major. After consulting a college counselor, I found I needed just four Economics credits from the University of California, Los Angeles to obtain my degree from Berkeley, as units were transferable.

At first I thought I would wait until summer, but decided I was tired of waiting — waiting to get better, waiting for my life to begin. The time was now. Three weeks later, I was sitting in a scoop-back seat in the fourth row of a large classroom, pen in hand, notebook open, soaking in a lecture on the Economics of Development — Econ124.

It wasn't that simple, really. U.C. schools never are. I was forced to arrange handicap parking, so I could park literally right outside my class. I battled the Admissions Department, UCLA Extension, and the Economics Department to be allowed enrollment in the class I wanted to take. I secured signatures and approvals, paid fees and filled out additional paperwork. But, I did it! And there I sat, long haired and skinny, the oldest guy in a class filled with college-age coeds that made me feel at times like a fish out of water, like I didn't belong, like maybe the other students thought there was something wrong with me.

But, most of the time, I just felt like me, like this was something I knew I had to complete, in the same way I'm sitting here writing this story. If you want to get your ideas out, be part of the world, you've got to get your college degree. Not because that's what my parents/advisors told me, but because that's the way it is in this world. At least it is here in the U.S., unless you're an exceptional talent, with an incredible dream. Even then, most of the time you need training.

To get my training, I dragged myself out of bed, drove

out to UCLA — tired if necessary — took notes, and asked questions. After class, I often walked over to a campus coffee shop and enjoyed a cup of mint tea, maybe a muffin or scone — real civilized — and did some reading; or simply relaxed and watched other students, teachers and visitors sit down/walk by. I pretended I was in every way like one of them, just another student, teacher, visitor enjoying a break after an hour-and-a-half of class, thinking about what it was I wanted to be when I was all grown up.

Summer came. I completed my first course and needed one more, so I enrolled in summer school, got the same parking arrangement, only this time, I was technically a full-time summer school student versus a student through UCLA extension. Classes were held every day versus twice a week.

My energy improved significantly from the day I first started back to school. Initially, I needed days off during the week to rest. Now I didn't. Initially, I felt overwhelmed by the daily schedule. Now I looked forward to it. My quiet afternoon hour in the coffee shop sipping hot tea, turned into a casual sunny afternoon on the grass drinking iced tea in the sculpture garden.

After finishing the course and submitting my final grades, I was notified I graduated from Berkeley, with a degree in Economics and a minor in Rhetoric.

"Mark, that's great news," my mom said over the phone. "Are you going to go through ceremonies next spring? It would be so wonderful if ..." blue cap and gown, me standing in a long line of fellow graduates as they read my name over the loudspeaker to a crowd of proud parents, supportive relatives and friends. My mom desperately wanted to see her son graduate.

"You know, Mom, all my friends are gone. And while I'm glad to have graduated, it just wouldn't be the same. I'd feel out of place going through ceremonies now."

Truth is, my graduating was somewhat anti-climactic. In mind and spirit, I had long since finished college — my degree merely the paper jacket on a book I'd already put down, set aside, to sit upon my shelf, which from time to time I'd pull down to reflect. College was Berkeley, my fraternity, playing rugby on Saturday afternoons with a group of guys I loved spending time with, partying at the local bars, studying in Doe and Moffitt libraries for that killer exam that always seemed to be around the next corner.

I was twenty-six years old when I finally graduated, not twenty-one. My triumphant return to Berkeley never materialized. I didn't even get my double major. Never graduated with friends.

Yet, all that mattered was that I finally obtained the degree I set out to obtain years before. The burden of making my way back to school was gone, lifted; no more albatross around my neck, camel on my back, stuck holding the Old Maid, fighting for shade in a desert seldom crossed, not a palm tree in sight. There would be no going back, which while sad, now meant I could focus all my energy on the future. I was moving forward, like everyone else I knew, a Curious George in an erstwhile zoo.

My certificate of graduation came in the mail. I knew what it was when I saw the letter. I opened it on the cement steps outside my house and simply stared at it for a while. No cheering crowds, no flashbulb memories ... yet no feeling quite compared to the satisfaction that welled up inside me. The moment passed, I folded it back up and carried it inside.

*C*hapter 26

This is the way the world starts. This is the way the world starts. This is the way my world starts — not with a bang, but with a bongo and a back-beat in a quiet coffee house, or was it a book store in Santa Monica?

I sat nervously in the audience, jitters in my gut, and watched/waited as one by one numbers drawn from a glass jar signaled the spoken-word artists it was their turn at the podium.

My poetry had grown large within me, like children in the belly of a pregnant mother. Or more like the swelling belly of a hungry child, because I was hungry for an audience. Looking for an outlet to release the angst pent up inside me, locked up and boxed up, I wanted freedom for my inhibited spirit. Spent the past five years telling myself I couldn't do this, couldn't do that, couldn't push myself, or overdo it.

But, it ran deeper than that. Imagine saying everything you ever wanted to say but didn't; acting out in every way you wanted to act out, but were afraid; becoming an entirely expressive being; singing out loud, in public, as a hundred thousand people cheered you on. You lay there writhing on a stage like an emphatic rock star, only drunk on life not alcohol/drugs.

That was the next stage — the stage. I wanted to stand up in front of a room of people and express myself, my ideas, my poetry; express my being as an audience watched, listened, then applauded.

I wanted the rush, to feel that intensity coursing

through me. I wanted to make an impact, be accepted. Deep down, I think I wanted to be famous. What is it about wanting to be famous, having people look at you, revere you, praise and hail, point and say, "Hey that's so-and-so. He was in such-and-such. And right now he's a somebody, something special."

You're not thinking about the people that stare. The looky-loos whos that watch and judge you. "He looks so much taller, smarter, better when you see him on TV/in the movies."

"Hey, can I have your autograph? I loved you in your movie. Congratulations on that punt, pass, catch, kick. That song you sing so sweet. I don't want you to sing for anyone but me." Which is when you start running into those sickos — those crazy people who shoot presidents and rock stars as a means of expressing their eternal devotion, like Kathy Bates in *Misery*, declaring "I'm your biggest fan!"

Can't imagine being famous, or even semi well-known. Too many people crowding around. They want to touch/feel you. They want a little piece of you, maybe stick their hand in your pants, watch you scream and dance. Ever wondered what that would be like?

I gave my first poetry reading on open-mike night at Midnight Special Books on the Santa Monica Promenade. You sign up and they draw your name randomly out of a hat.

It was getting late and the waiting made me tired, sitting on fold-down metal seats as pensive minds watched and listened attentively. Wood floors with pictures and books lined the walls; people turned to look at people coming in and out, who stayed to hear a few of the poets before carrying on their way back into the street, the shuffling feet, the sound of pages turning, the scrawl of pens on scratchpads.

They called my name. My body tingled as I stepped up to the podium, lights and eyes staring up at me. "Little Darling," I began, as I read my poem of Oedipal devotion toward my mother. Soft voice in a quiet room, I felt like I was standing in isolation, the moment suspended, the

219

audience waiting for me to throw on the switch so everyone could start moving again.

When I finished, I looked up to see the audience
applauding. I smiled, walked off the stage, and sat down.
I thought I carried it well, though I wasn't sure. I had to
ask the friend I came with for some reassurance.

"So, what did you think? How'd I do up there?"

"You did great. I thought you were one of the best
ones up there. You had a presence about you. It wasn't
overdone, or underdone. You were really great."

And maybe those were bias words, but maybe not.
I was just amazed I pulled it off. As we walked out of the
bookstore, I felt different than when I walked in. Like
there were new springs fixed to the bottom of my black
leather boots, and I was skippin' along. I felt alive,
empowered by an audience of people who listened attentively as I spoke, then applauded when I was finished
simply because I had the courage to stand up in front of
them. I was out there, my name in the hat, vying for a sliv-
er of limelight.

It felt right, so I just kept going. I gave readings in
bars, coffee houses, and bookstores all over the city.
Invited my friends sometimes, but I'd usually go alone.
This was my thing, done entirely for me.

When I brought friends, a part of me wanted to please
them. Wanted them to like/accept the new me, my poetry.
I wanted them to think I was good and to tell me they
thought I was good. Most were supportive, but there's
always someone who wants to be a critic. They think
they're being helpful. Or perhaps their petty jealousies
have gotten the best of them — "I could do that. Next
time, maybe I'll get up there and just say what's on my
mind." Then do it, but spare me your insecurities and get
off my cloud. I've got my own emotional self-doubts to
contend with.

Most of the time I went alone, standing before a nameless, semi-recognizable crowd: semi-recognizable because
I saw the same people out at the places I frequented;
nameless, because I kept to myself. Didn't want to worry
about who they were, what they thought. I read, sat down,

then walked out as anonymous as when I walked in.

Sure, I sometimes struck up a conversation here and there: "Hey, how's it going? I saw you at such and such. Ever been out to ..." But, most of the time, I sat alone and said little. My anonymity enabled me to be whoever I wanted to be, say whatever I wanted to say, and act however I felt like acting. My anonymity freed me to be completely myself.

Wasn't long before I started taking my guitar out with me, too. I waited patiently to perform over music and mint tea. "And next up, number twenty-three ... Mark Hall." Guitar slung over my shoulder, hair down, I was just another dude with an attitude, albeit friendly and cordial. I strolled up to the small stage, a confident smile on my face; plugged in my guitar, so I was electric; and started strumming, hips swaying back and forth, black boots tapping. I'd lean into the mike and sing:

I know a man with a million dollar mind
he's got million dollar houses
he drinks million dollar wine,
all his women merely satisfy his ego
they're a physical extension of his masculine libido,
this man he hates himself he tried to take his life
he would have died if it wasn't for his wife
you know she found him in the basement
eating sleeping pills for breakfast
it's a high price to pay for material success

I know a woman with that sultry look of freedom
wears a leather jacket, her pants are painted denim
she's sitting in a coffee house sipping cappuccino
smokin' lots of cigarettes, she claims she is enlightened,
this woman's angry at a world that failed to ground her
she's raging at society around her, she says,
"The rich they are all tyrants, the government is tired,
the streets are filled with violence"
I say, "Oh you're so inspired!"

hide, hide, hide, yeah play your games
hide, hide, hide, it always stays the same

221

see the family walking across the street
that boy is crying, his parents took his treats
his mama says, "Boy, you better shut up"
she takes her hand and she smacks him
the boy says, "I don't need you, I don't need you"
the dad laughs, he says, "Who is going to feed you?"
the boy says, "I am leaving don't mistake it,
laugh now, but fuck you when I make it"

hide, hide, hide, yeah play your little games
hide, hide, hide, nothing's going to change
hide, hide, hide, put on your facade and
hide, hide, hide, but you'll wear it 'til you die

There was this incredible feeling, when someone from the crowd, or better yet, one of the other musicians/poets, would walk over to me after I finished and say, "Man, that was great."

And I would say, "Cool, thanks. I appreciate it."

I would drive home singing my lungs out, or spewing poem after poem in my car, foot heavy on the gas, until my voice grew hoarse and I felt a little light-headed. I'd dance up the steps to my room, my fears, doubts and phobias taking the night off; better yet, vacationing in Siberia.

*C*hapter 27

What does it mean to be happy? What does it mean to be healthy? Sane? Fulfilled? By what measure should we consider ourselves so? If a pontiff or patriarch tells us we are happy, then are we happy? If a doctor decides we are for all practical purposes healthy, then are we healthy? Who decides these arbitrary definitions? How do we determine them for ourselves? Do we sit back and look at the rest of society as a barometer to which we compare ourselves then determine where we fit in? Is that an accurate measure? Or do we look inside and try to determine these values for ourselves? Would a schizophrenic be a good judge of his/her own wellness/sanity?

For years I searched for this ideal called perfect health. Yet, how many people really are healthy? Either they've got a bad back, stomachache, the flu, chronic pain, asthma, allergy attacks, ringworm, lice, and fleas; not to mention cancer, diabetes, and that dormant, oh quite nefarious bedfellow — AIDS.

I guess your definition of "perfect health" might be "disease-free." I want to be disease-free, but then that depends on what your definition of disease really is. I know people disease-free, suffocating in unhealthy relationships; spiritual selves lifeless and gone, suffering from workaholism, struggling to get ahead. Angry, frustrated, tired, reckless, insecure, despised, despondent, cantankerous, chaotic, neurotic, listless, uncivil and grieved, and these are some of the supposedly happier people I know. Are they healthy?

Rapes and scars, hurts and shame, never met a man or woman whose existence was entirely free of pain. Even Christ, recognized as one of the most evolved humans (and there are many who say he wasn't human at all, but a god, or the son of God, and yet aren't we all sons and daughters of God, perhaps he was the eldest son — big brother so to speak) was not entirely content with his life. On the day Pontius Pilate crucified him, Christ yells skyward from the cross, "Father, Father, why hast though forsaken me?" — which is precisely the same question I had for Him, grand pooh-bah in the sky. I might as well take a number, and get in line.

I took a trip into paradise — two thousand miles from Los Angeles to Cancun, where Alex and I rendezvoused to enjoy the white sand beaches and blue-green ocean of the Mexican Gulf Coast; a chance to escape the lives we struggled through at home.

We stayed in her parents' two-story, beach-front condo — palm fronds and geckos on a tropical terrace that overlooked the water. Riding in the cab from the Cancun airport, the air hot and humid, the scenery slipped by like a warm shower. Took a lot of courage for me to take this trip. I was used to sticking close to home, yet here I was stepping into the unknown. It felt incredible to be there.

I checked in at the front desk, carried my bags upstairs, unpacked my clothes and waited eagerly for Alex to arrive.

She was late, her plane delayed. When she finally arrived, her feelings were much the same as mine — excitement, joy, bliss.

"Mark, isn't this incredible? Can you believe we're actually here together?"

"I can't, because this isn't happening. I've been here four-and-a-half hours and I'm convinced this is just some sick hoax that God or maybe the Devil is playing on us."

"Very funny. Have you been down to the beach?"

"Not yet."

"Have you been out to the pool?"

"No, I've been waiting for you."

"What do you think of the view?"

"I think it's extremely cool."

For seven days and six nights, we ate dinner in town; took day trips to Xcaret, Xel-Ha, Xpu-Ha and the ruins at Tulum. We took a ferry ride to Isla Mujeres, where we rented mopeds for the day and toured the island.

We were walking back late one night from an evening at the Hard Rock Cafe ... Don't ask why we spent an evening in this hub of first world kitsch, or why we weren't out learning to lambada instead. There was a local band playing covers of The Plimsouls and Elvis in his early days. Going out to party was something we never really did together. As if I owe you an explanation.

So, getting back to walking back late one night, we laid down just off the path in a grassy park the other side of the condos where we stayed. The wind was wild, warm and wonderful. Palm trees swayed and rustled, while we made love, as Alex put it, "decadently underneath the moon."

Despite our day-long incredible trips in a rented Volkswagon down the coast to go snorkeling, and tour archeological ruins of ancient cities still standing an astounding 1,200 hundred years after abandonment; despite our pleasure walks along the soft sand shore, candlelight dinners and midnight jacuzzis, while the families staying in our complex were asleep; despite all this (my dear, might I have one last kiss) our relationship began to unravel.

On the first day, we shrugged off our differences. On the second day, we bickered and fought. By the third day, few words passed between us. By the fourth day, our relationship was clearly over. We slept in separate rooms desperately wanting the week to end, when we could run home, cry about and put behind us a vacation/love affair gone terribly awry.

Looking back, I still don't know what happened, or how it happened so quickly. It hit us like that one drink too many on a bar room afternoon in the sun. I guess it took the perfect romantic vacation — our first major undertaking as a couple — to realize our relationship was not as perfect as we thought, hoped, or perhaps envisioned.

Alex and I wanted different things. She was looking

for a man to take care of her, which was a problem given I could barely take care of myself. She knew the situation regarding my illness, and yet I think she deluded herself into believing I really wasn't that sick.

"Wow, what a day," I said. "I'm beat. Why don't we just kick back tonight."

"What do you mean kick back?" she said. "You don't want to go out?"

"Like I said, I'm pretty tired. I know we're planning another big day. I want to take it easy so I have enough energy for tomorrow. Aren't you tired?"

"A little. So, I was going to shower, then get ready to go." At which point, she snapped. "You know, I came down here to enjoy myself. I don't want to stay cooped up inside the entire trip. I do enough of that at home."

"What are you talking about, we've been out all day."

"I know, but why should that stop us from going out tonight? I'm sick of always having to take it easy, because you don't feel up to doing things. I just think it's really selfish. You know the world doesn't revolve around you. Couldn't you just make an exception this once? Couldn't we just go out this one time, when I really need to go out? Is that too much to ask? Is it? Is it?!!!"

Sure, Alex was a little unstable while on our trip. She was on new medication that made her edgy, endured months of being holed up, hiding out at home; not to mention mounting frustrations we both shared regarding the possibility of a future together; questions about the ten-year age difference between us; difficulties we both faced in our lives — issues of money, location, and uncertainty as to whether we were even compatible.

And sure, I'm probably leaving a little out, like the fact that we hadn't really been getting along the entire day. Still, the more time we spent together, the more it became apparent Alex enjoyed certain activities and went about doing them in a manner exactly contrary to the activities I enjoyed doing and the way I went about doing them.

"Look, it's pretty clear you're set on going out. I feel like taking it easy tonight. Why don't you just go out by yourself?" I finally said.

"I think I will," she replied, our relationship deteriorating drastically into anger, rage and rant.

Riding the shuttle bus back to the airport, I felt angry, confused, but mostly sad and unsure of how I would handle the breakup. Not yet certain of what I had lost. We said we'd be friends, but I had said that before to lovers who disappeared like dying suns, collapsing into darkness.

An older woman, who watched us part, leaned over my seat once the bus started moving and said, "Don't be sad. Everything's going to be all right. You'll see her again."

"I don't think I will."

"Of course you will," she said. "In the meantime, you can think of the wonderful time you had together," which of course made me feel worse. I slumped down in my seat and stared out the window, grieving the loss of my friend — watched the trees, shrubs, sea, sand, asphalt flying by.

I wish I could hand you the world on a string
and breathe magic into everything you see
I think the clouds of you,

I wish I could build you a house by a lake
and take you away from the things that take you from me
I think the stars of you,

I'm wishing we were meant to be
we talk in different languages
the other hasn't learned to speak
"Come into my garden," I say
you just turn and walk away
"Step on through my pasture," you scream
but I listen to the words in between

wishing we were meant to be
wishing we were meant to be

I wish I could take you into my heart
and show you a friend who's never going to leave
I feel the oceans for you

Dazed And Fatigued

I wish I could waltz you from here to the moon
and the earth stood still
as I sang you a tune from my knees
you know, it's all about you
I'm wishing we were meant to be
we talk in different languages
the other hasn't learned to speak
"Bathe beneath my fountain," I whine
you just turn your head and cry
"Tumble down my meadow," you scream
but I listen to the words in between

wishing we were meant to be
wishing we were meant to be

*C*hapter 28

Back in L.A. the sticks were somewhat scrambled, the channels fuzzy and mixed up. I continued to give readings, sing and play guitar on open-mike nights in coffee houses and clubs around town.

I went to my friend Drew's wedding — a weekend bash, where everyone descended on Lake Tahoe. They flew in and drove in. We shared rented condos on the lake, played hoops and had fun just like we did when we all went to Berkeley together.

A former rugby teammate, Drew was two years older than I and had been my pledge father in our fraternity house. Lindy, his fiancée, was the best friend and sorority sister of my college girlfriend, Jennifer. Strange to think we set them up way back when and now they were getting married.

Stranger still to see my former girlfriend at the wedding after such a long time. She looked just as I remembered her, except her long blond hair was now a little longer; still tanned and attractive. With her nice clothes and a charming smile, Jen was a very classy young woman. She always had been, just like the pictures in photo albums from my college years; pictures I went through at least a hundred times since my illness first began — flipping through, reminiscing like an old quarter-back reliving his glory days.

We spoke for the first time standing in line for dinner at the reception held the night before the wedding. Dinner was a buffet, served in the party room of an elegant restaurant overlooking the lake. Having dished up our food, a collection of pastas, salads, fish, and bread, we sat down at a table with Jennifer's former sorority sisters, pampered and perfumed.

While Jen and I went to grab drinks, a couple spots opened up at the larger tables, to which Jen's friends quickly migrated — more people, laughter, men. We came back to find we'd be dining alone — candlelight reflecting off the glass, through which you could see silhouettes of pine trees and the black expanse of water in the distance.

Romantic? Might have been, but for the years blown wickedly by. Jen and I were simply two old friends catching up. I was excited to see her. She had been such a significant part of my life, and I was eager to hear how her life had progressed.

The only problem was that I expected to talk to the person I knew five years before; the same person I spent days, weeks, months, years of my time with, going to parties and shows, laughing on the way to the library, arguing because she felt I was a little underdressed for the dinner we would be having with her parents.

Jen and I had history together. She looked the same. Her mannerisms were the same. She enjoyed drinking the glass of chardonnay the same way she always had when we went out and ate dinner together. I instantly felt comfortable with her.

Yet, she wasn't the same at all, or maybe she was and my values had changed so much that our belief systems were completely incongruous. I can only imagine what she thought of me, but there I sat, listening as she spoke proudly of her brand new BMW. She talked about the boyfriend whom she broke up with just days before Drew's wedding, because she found out that for the entire duration of their relationship, he had been seeing another girl on the side.

"Are you seeing anyone?" I said, mid-way through dinner.

"Actually, I was seeing this guy, but we just broke up a few days ago."

"What happened?"

"Well, about two weeks ago this girl calls me and says she wants me to know she's been seeing Brad (the guy I've been dating) for the past year, that she's always known that I was the wife, so to speak, and she the mistress, but that she felt I should know."

"Were you planning on marrying this guy?"

"No. But, we dated for a while and obviously talked about it."

"So, you were serious enough to talk about marriage and yet you had no idea he was dating another girl?"

"Maybe I suspected, but I really didn't know."

"How is that possible? I mean I understand not knowing about a one night stand, but it sounds like he's been dating her for a long time."

"Well, how was I to know?"

"In my relationships I try to maintain such an open dialogue and know them so well it would be virtually impossible not to know."

"I guess that was one of the problems. He never really seemed that sincere."

"Then why did you go out with him so long?"

"He was an impressive guy. Always traveled first class. Ate in the best restaurants."

I'm thinking: this is an intelligent woman telling me this. Am I the only one who sees something wrong here?

We changed the subject and she started talking about her job and her life in Manhattan Beach, which if you've never been to southern California is home to the upwardly mobile, young professional/post-collegiate frat-guy, sorority crowd. Glass houses overlook the sand, where the only pronouns most residents can find to use are "I" and "me," as they pay lip-service to global consciousness, when what they'd really like to do is eradicate the world of everything foreign and lesser than clean, sipping down mai-tai's, you know the scene.

Maybe I'm a little biased. Sure, there are a few enlightened souls who live there, but in general my critique is right on. Peek under the surface, nothing's there but a little whitewash and a shallow grave filled with ideas that died before they could become original. Oops! There goes vicious little me again, now who am I to criticize? What do I know? Just a guy with a computer and a lot of crazy ideas. Let's get back to the story ...

I listened as Jen told me about the cancer that for a few months threatened to take her mother's life — something Drew and Lindy mentioned that saddened me. Jen's mom had always been extremely kind to me. I wanted to be compassionate; wanted to let her know I understood, at least on some level, the type of fear Jen must have experienced as a result of her mother's illness.

Yet, the entire time, Jennifer kept implying her mother's cancer was far more serious than the illness I had: "I mean, she had cancer. She almost died. You know, you've got to come to terms with this illness of yours, stop feeling sorry for yourself and get on with your life." Kept implying that if only I possessed the determination her mother had, maybe I would get better, too.

This brought me back to the weeks just prior to our final break-up, in which she showed so little compassion, and offered virtually no support. Now I was forced to listen to her pontificate on the current state of the country, the violence and the need to keep all those sickos and druggies off the streets; problems with illegal immigration and the need to ship those border-jumping vagrants back where they came from — better yet, let's just shoot 'em and forget about it.

Again, I'm probably exaggerating. I can't remember exactly what she said, but I couldn't help thinking by the end of the evening that Jennifer was a modern-day Marie Antoinette. So completely out of touch with reality, so lacking in all form of compassion for people, so blind and deluded — must be the glare of the sun off the glass, sand, water in that comfortable beach town she lived in — that I wanted to stand up, shake her by the shoulders and scream, "Open your eyes, you ignorant bitch!"

More disturbing still, was the fact that by the look on her face, I could tell she was thinking the exact same thing about me.

At the wedding the following day, I saw a lot of people

I knew, faces I hadn't seen in a long time. Mostly the people were Drew's age — a couple years older than myself. Long explanations regarding what I was up to, how I felt. Many heard through the grapevine about my illness, and most were glad to see I was recovering from it.

Drew's was the second wedding I went to that summer. The first was the wedding of one of my closest friends from high school. I enjoyed seeing the people, the old friends and familiar faces. Yet, I found it hard to see them and to hear about the things they were doing, the places they visited, the jobs they held.

They had all advanced into the working world and were busy spending time and effort to make names for themselves, and earn an extravagant living. Many of them found success and were making good money. Others were in medical school, or just finishing business school having worked on Wall Street or somewhere off in Hong Kong, London, Central America. Many had traveled the world.

At the same time, it was interesting to see in most cases how little their lives had changed. Many lived in San Francisco or Los Angeles, hung out with the same friends they hung out with in high school or college. Several of the guys I played rugby with were still playing with clubs in the Bay Area. They had girlfriends or wives, jobs, apartments, condos, houses. They were basically exactly the same people I remembered them being, espousing the exact same ideas/beliefs, only now they held working world jobs, balanced working world schedules, and lived working world lifestyles with all the anxiety, independence and responsibility that came with their new roles/titles.

For the most part, I was seeing these people for the first time since before my illness began. Made me somewhat envious to think about all the adventures they experienced and I was only just now graduating from college, starting to look for my first job with no real idea of what I would do next.

Had I graduated when I was *supposed to*, I probably would have pursued a path similar to the old friends and acquaintances I saw at these weddings — something business related, chasing the green/my dreams at the same time.

Through my illness, my interests changed. I enjoyed playing guitar and writing. I had really long hair. While one side of me was still interested in business, high finance, numbers and money and suit and tie and shiny shoes, hair parted, driving a sporty car, the other side of me decided that a job in the business world was exactly what I wasn't interested in. I wanted to be a writer and a musician. I wanted to perform onstage, and escape the cage I felt awaited me working nine-to-five, nine-to-six-seven-eight, day in day out, trudging to an office, strapped down like a man in a straitjacket for the rest of my life, dirty dancing with the Devil's wife.

"If that's my fate," I proclaimed, "then go ahead and slit my wrists right now, because I'd rather be dead than be one of the walking dead."

Before deciding on anything, I took a trip to New York to visit my friends Jay and Nick — a treat to congratulate myself for graduating. Jay, my former writing partner, and I stayed in very close contact. We talked almost daily to discuss the writing projects we were working on; the confusion that went along with me looking for a place in my future and he trying to establish a new life in New York, working as a journalist for the Wall Street Journal.

Nick was my phone friend — a friend I never met beyond conversations we shared as a result of the chronic fatigue illness that plagued us both. I looked forward to meeting him in person for the first time. I looked forward to the experience of visiting New York, a place I had never been; kicking around the Big Apple, a city that bustled with energy, ideas, people, late-night restaurants and all-night bars; a city that never slept, only laid awake weeping into the wee hours before starting fresh again the next day on coffee and donuts.

I split my time equally between my two friends, going first to a movie with one, then taking in dinner and drinks — though I still didn't drink — with the other. This seemed to work well, as they had very different schedules, led very different lives: one a writer, the other a singer/actor/performer; one employed on a regular

234

working schedule, the other running from auditions, to workouts, to acting classes.

Meeting Nick for the first time was a little strange. We each created this image of what the other looked like based on the stories we told one another, and the descriptions we supplied. You expect someone to look and act one way, only to discover they look and act completely different. He, for some reason thought my hair was fair, even though I told him it was dark. I, for some reason, thought he would have darker features — darker hair, darker skin, etc. — even though I actually saw a video of him performing. Interesting to see how we each thought the other would look more like ourselves.

But, there was more to it than that. Nick was tense, grown more tense as a result of his illness that stole from him so many of the things he worked toward and cherished. When he first got sick, his band had just been signed to a record label. He felt he was finally on his way to the top. The video I saw was of him and his band performing on the Jay Leno show.

After the show taped, Nick suffered a relapse. He often complained that the medications he took affected his singing voice. Some days he called contemplating suicide.

The days he felt good enough to be out were like a whirlwind of activity for him, going to auditions, going to acting class, working out, running errands — frantic in every way. The pages of his day planner were scrawled with notes and activities crossed out and added on. During some time slots he would double-book activities just in case he finished his primary concern early and had some time to spare.

As we walked the streets together, Nick was wild and uninhibited, leaping in front of virtually every girl we saw to ask her out, see if they wanted to have coffee sometime. Sometimes he'd stop, turn around, cross the street and start back the other way simply to ask a girl's name and get a phone number so he could call her later.

"Hey, how's it going? I'm Nick. Are you walking this way?"

"Yes." Giggle. Smile. Confusion.

"Mind if I walk with you?" he asks, crowding her space.

"Sure ... okay ... ?" as she starts to veer sideways, but not always. A couple times he'd come running back, phone number in hand, excited and gay, looking for his next, "Hey, how's it going?"

"How many girls would you say you ask out each day?" I asked him one night.

"About ten."

"And how many do you actually end up going out with?"

"Sometimes one or two. Sometimes I don't get a date all week, because most of the girls I walk up to blow me off, probably because they think I'm coming off too desperate. You should have seen this girl I asked out last week. She was sitting in a bar as I walked by and saw her through the window. She was so beautiful, I walked in and asked her out. She was really flattered ..."

"Did you end up going out with her?"

"Not yet, but we're supposed to get together."

"Pretty bold."

"I can't help it. It's like I've got to talk to them."

"Yeah, and if just one in fifty girls ends up going out with you, that's a date a week."

"Never really thought of it that way, but you're right. If only I could get one in fifty." Laughter. Ha-Ha.

Nick was a guy who loved life, only so long as he was out in it, interacting with the people, the places; seizing every minute, else it be stolen like cash and a wallet full of credit cards.

I, on the contrary, was someone wild and tense grown reserved as a result of my illness. I was unsure of my steps, with each new step sending a wave of fear through my psyche. "Would this one be too far, the one that sends me spiraling back into wilderness and the oblivion of an illness that might never end?"

Though some of my former confidence returned with my improving health, I carried these fears with me on a daily basis. I was always checking myself, asking myself, "How are you feeling now? And now? How about now?"

In a way, I blamed, albeit falsely, my gregarious nature as the cause of my illness. I believed that if I were a bit more cautious, a little less wild, and a little more responsible, maybe I would never have become sick in the first place.

As Nick and I perused the city, he aggressively trying to win back every minute lost to illness and I trying to avoid in every way the pitfalls of my free unbridled spirit, our neuroses would at times clash. His relentless girl-chasing would force me to sit down, take a few deep breaths and collect myself. At the same time, my frequent probing as to how far a particular restaurant, bar, or subway stop was and how much walking was entailed forced him to hasten his pace a little and come up with yet another thing we could do to extend our evening into the following day, like eating pre-dawn breakfasts in a small but crowded coffee shop full of vampires and night owls a few blocks south of Harlem.

Jay lived on Curry Row, a block concentrated with Indian restaurants in the Lower East Village of Manhattan. His third story walk-up apartment had a "convenience" kitchen (nothin' convenient about a convenience kitchen I assure you — two electric stove-top burners, a few cabinets and a refrigerator the size of something you might find on a Winnebago). The shower was situated not in the bathroom, but in the middle of the apartment, half-way between the living room and Jay's sleeping area.

The apartment's worst feature was also its best. A small window which overlooked the back alley allowed so little light, that artificial lighting was required even on sunny days. Yet, the window opened onto a fire escape that led to the roof, and offered a view of the midtown skyscrapers and dingy asphalt streets below.

Coming from Los Angeles, I was always impressed with how close-by everything was in other large cities I visited. In New York, for example, no driving was necessary. A laundromat, market, local burrito stand and subway stop — the gateway to Manhattan — were just a few minutes' walk from Jay's front door.

While Nick took me through Soho, the Upper West

Side, and a small club where his friend's band played, Jay and I toured the East Village, Chinatown, the Barnes & Noble bookstore on Fifth Avenue and shot hoops at the local park.

I spent hours roaming the city on my own. I walked the shops up Fifth Avenue. I spent an afternoon in Central Park, admiring the splendor in the grass, then headed downtown to Wall Street, and spent an evening playing carnival games at a street festival in Little Italy.

Yet, I merely breached the surface, like skipping stones. How can anyone take in all of New York in six days, or expect to, or even want to? Too many dark alleys, uncharted zones, mom and pop shops, restaurants and clubs evolving/revolving so quickly. Four hundred new restaurants apply for licenses each year. If you ate in a different restaurant every night of the week, you could never eat in all the *new* restaurants opened in New York City each year, not to mention those already existing. Like viral mutations, it's impossible to keep up with all the latest trends; the fashionable, historical, multi-cultural, modern, post-modern industrial, glitz, yeah — lots of glitz, no way for even local residents to keep up with everything.

I was glad to be in New York, glad for the freedom I felt and the friendships I shared. When it came time to go, I wasn't ready to leave, but I couldn't stay either. My health was stabilizing, yet still somewhat shaky — no job, no income, the responsibility/luxury of having to take care of my mom's house.

Before I left, I took time to say goodbye to my friends. Shared a cab with a stranger on my way to the airport, where I boarded a Boeing 747, big bird in the sky, soaring higher and higher.

"Seat 27B, that's down the right aisle. And you're down the left aisle ... right ... left ... right ... left ..." like being in the military, taking orders, following rules, regulations — the hierarchical politics of a plane flight. Sounds like a potential essay topic, and a bad one at that.

I arrived home after my long trip and sat down to relax my feet, crawled into bed and started to read. Before I knew it, I was fast asleep enjoying my best night's rest in a week.

*C*hapter 29

New York was a tremendous breakthrough for me. I always tended to do well on trips; tended to find reserves of energy I didn't know were in me. It marked the first time I felt free to do essentially everything I wanted. Enjoy myself instead of worrying. I felt strong, healthy, and remarkably alive, like I turned the corner, flipped the switch of floodlights that set the stage for wellness.

In New York I met a girl, another girl, this one named Marisol. She traveled the world, or at least half of it as she flew from the Philippines, where she was born and raised, to Michigan, then New York. She lived in Manhattan four years; attended, then graduated from the Fashion Institute of Technology to work two years in the garment industry.

Marisol was friends with Jay. We met and talked for more than an hour at an apartment party on Second Avenue. The fact she grew up in the Philippines intrigued me and gave us something to talk about, as I recounted scenes from the screenplay I was writing; the mindwalks I took through the backstreets of Manila and along the coastal highways of the Philippine countryside.

"Tell me about the beaches," I said, "and about the tropical flora and fauna. Tell me about Mount Pinatubo, Bicol, Makati, where you grew up, the people, customs, textures." I wanted to hear about all the places I imagined, but never saw.

But, Marisol's experience living in the Philippines did not resemble the mysterious Eden my fantasies conjured. Her parents were well-off, but her childhood was far from

239

perfect. The disparity between rich and poor that forced a majority of the population to live in poverty and squalor disturbed her. The close-knit society that was on one hand comforting, and on the other created a situation where everyone knows who's doing what, with whom and how often, most of the time, crowded her individuality and sense of freedom. At twenty-one she left because she had to. Came to the States to live with her brother, who left a few years before.

Amazing what people tell me in an evening. Deep secrets, like I'm their therapist or like I've known them for years. Share with me your sorrow, your laughter, and your tears. Tell me your troubles, I'll tell you my fears. She did, and we bonded in the fifteenth floor apartment, sitting in the living room on bar stools, crowded by party guests. Rain poured down outside. She was headed to Los Angeles to spend a few months with her brother, who lived in Palos Verdes with his wife and two kids. I gave her my phone number and told her to call me when she got into town. We could have lunch, go out, give her something to do in between visits to Disneyland, Magic Mountain, Universal Studios, and the Zoo.

"Hello, is Mark there?"

"This is Mark"

"Hi Mark, it's Marisol."

"Marisol! Are you in Los Angeles?"

"Uh-huh ... I've been here for about a week."

"Taking in the sights? What have you been doing?"

"Not much, really. I've been to the beach, Disneyland, and this weekend we're going to Universal Studios."

"Having a good time?"

"Yeah, it's nice to be on vacation."

"That's great. Would you like to get together while you're here? We could grab some dinner, or maybe you could come to one of my open-mike's."

"Okay."

"How about dinner this Thursday?"

"Sounds good."

"All right. Why don't you give me directions to your brother's place and I'll come and pick you up ... Uh-huh ...

240

Uh-huh ... Then make a left on Hawthorne? Okay, great, I'll give you a call before I come."

Was I that cool? No way — women made me nervous. Confidence so low, I had to scrape it like flapjacks from the pavement sometimes. Still, I had my moments, once I got comfortable. My nervousness that built up like a tremor — needles tickling/trickling up my spine — generally subsided and I could be myself, could communicate passionately. Why communicate if you've got nothing to be passionate about? Unless of course you're asking for directions, or a glass of water. Then to be passionate you'd merely be making a fool of yourself: "Can I [hesitate, gesticulate] have [inhale deeply, sigh] a glass [smile warmly] of water? [collapse into repose]"

The situation around my getting a job was two-fold, or three, or four, but who's counting? Here were the two main issues. As I mentioned before, I didn't really want to work, at least not in the nine-to-five sense; not in the grind I watched suck life from my mom and dad — workaholics, struggling to get ahead and get to the point that almost never comes, when they could say, "Whew, I've made it. Now I can relax and enjoy the rest of my life peacefully."

Meanwhile, you're sixty-five. What's left to enjoy? Too busy worrying about the stress-related heart attack you had two years ago. Add this to the fact you probably forgot what it means to relax and enjoy. You've been going so hard for so long. So achievement-oriented, you're trying to figure out the "best" way to "manage" your golden years to get the "most" out of the rest of your life.

I learned the hard way what it meant to suffer burnout — been burned out of society altogether five long years. Didn't want to suffer that midlife crisis, that late life stroke on top of the suffering I already endured. I knew better.

Yet, I wanted to earn money, be able to support myself, get off disability income and survive on my own. Most importantly, I wanted to prove to myself I could do it. I saw working as the last signpost on my road to recovery — the final hurdle. Once I had a job, and was able maintain that job from a health perspective, not only would I be healthy, I would be normal.

Normal people worked. In fact, normal people not only worked long days, but worked out at the end of long days, then maybe went out to take in a movie, enjoy some swingin' blues, toss back a few beers at the local pub. Glub, chug-a-lug.

By taking and maintaining a job, I would be like every other Tom, Dick, Moe — a face in the crowd, fighting his way through the ranks on his way up the ladder to achieve success in the eyes of his peers.

You should have heard the voices of approval, the physical pats on the back:

"I finally graduated, now I'm looking for a job."

"That's great. Are you completely better?"

"Pretty much. I'd say I'm about ninety-five percent better. I still get tired sometimes, but I think I'm basically there."

"After all this time, that's fantastic. How's the job search going?"

"All right. It's frustrating at times."

"Yeah, I know. Job hunting is the worst. I remember right before I got this job ..."

First time in five years, I was actually talking to people in general about a stage in my life they could relate to — the dreaded job search — networking, cover letters, interviews, and rejections.

I actually enjoyed complaining. When I did, I no longer saw the uncomfortable faces of friends/strangers who could not understand. Instead they nodded, smiled, shook their heads knowingly and stood there sharing war stories, complaining of the irony and the agony they endured before landing their jobs.

Sure, from time to time I got that occasional, "Yeah, I know how hard getting a job can be. I got really lucky. It only took me two weeks." Because everyone wants to consider himself/herself an anomaly — the one who got lucky. In which case, they're more than happy to share their advice. The entire time I'm thinking, "Give me a break. I've been sick all this time. Miracle I even fucking graduated and now on top of all this, I have to listen to you, who, in two short weeks, happened to get lucky!"

Rebirth

Not that I was complaining. It's just that luck had been a commodity in short supply, where my inelastic demand created a Keynesian catastrophe if you will. Seemed like everything I did, I worked, toiled and struggled for, like a dina-sour trudging through tar pits, vainly trying to get unstuck. Nothing came easy.

Job hunting was no different. Most frustrating was this dichotomy between who I once was, which included the coursework I studied in school — Business, Rhetoric, Economics — and who I had become as a result of my illness — creative, pensive, cautious, a poet in search of enlightenment.

To help rectify my confusion, I went to see a career counselor — someone to give insight to my true path, my inner calling, or at least offer some advice on which direction to take.

With Iris, I talked about possible career opportunities, endured profile testing, and tried to match my skills against a Help-Wanted section of the Los Angeles Times that despite its numerous listings seemed sparse at best. We talked about strategies for landing the perfect job, ways to research, and what to expect.

I was twenty-six years old trying to land my first real job. Like most students just graduating from college, I was looking for ways to start right at the top and hopscotch over the years I lost to illness. Yet, the more time we spent together — Iris and I — the more confused I became. Every job I read about sounded the same, and elicited that all-too-familiar cringe and comment: "No way do I want to do that;" and "You expect me to start off doing what?"

In a way I was fortunate, as virtually every resume I sent out landed me an interview. From mid-level university staff positions to coveted entry-level investment banking and consulting firm positions, everybody I met with wanted to meet a guy who studied Economics and Business, had played rugby and was a poet/writer in his alter-/altered life.

Problem was, the people I met with were looking for a long-term commitment, when for the past five years I hadn't been able to commit to a day at the movies. They

243

wanted straightforward answers and to ascertain from their interviewee a sense of continuity. They wanted to talk to those who set out in the prime of their collegiate careers studying a major, then working a few high-profile internships, and now having graduated with the intent that the job they applied for represented the obvious culmination of all they set out to achieve. The Business major goes on to a career in business. The Art History major goes on to work in a Soho gallery or realizes his/her affinity for painting. The English major goes to law school or flies off to teach English as a second language in Kyoto, Japan.

They wanted to package you, and to know the package all made sense; the youthful enthusiasm that says to the interviewer you're willing to accept half of what you're worth, and work twice the hours for which you are paid; the naiveté on your face revealing that your world up to this point has worked out exactly, or almost exactly the way you thought it would.

Unlike everyone else I knew who graduated after four, even five years of college, my world hadn't gone exactly as planned, or even close for that matter. While I tended to start off with the quick quips in casual conversation they were looking for, as the interview progressed, my responses became less patent, more thought-out. Easy questions drew philosophical replies, sometimes ridiculously unrelated to the response my interviewer was driving toward:

"Sounds like you have some solid ideas, Mark, and a good understanding of what we do here. What are your long-term goals? Where do you plan to be in five or ten years?"

"My life is so different now than it was five years ago. How could I possibly predict where I'll be five years from today? I'm just looking for an opportunity to learn as much as I possibly can."

"But you have to have an idea. Everyone has goals — long term plans."

"I do have goals. I'd like to have a family. I'd like to lead a peaceful comfortable life, maybe start my own business at some point down the road. But, to say that ten years from now, I'm going to be doing this, or doing that.

Why cheat myself into envisioning a reality that may never come, or follow a path that in five years won't interest me at all?"

"Well, I think that about wraps things up. Thanks for coming in, Mark. We'll probably call you."

"Sure. It was a pleasure meeting you."

Meltdown! I could feel the interview slipping away from me. I could feel the rejection coming on. Rejection after rejection in a string of rejections on a search, in which, I pursued jobs an industry at a time.

Each interview I went on, I wanted to tell them about my miracle, about my struggle through five years of illness: the long cold winter I endured in Toronto; the days I was too weak to walk outside; the knowledge and wisdom I gained along the way. I wanted to tell them about my recovery, the most significant event in my life — my greatest achievement, my richest learning experience, the one event that impacted me the most.

Yet, I couldn't, because I knew that in the working world, a world of competition and greed, the wisdom I gained and the achievements I made weren't even valued. It wasn't even as if I overcame leukemia, paralysis — something glamorous, some highly publicized illness that, when they know you have it, they immediately stop and say, "That's terrible. That's absolutely terrible. Is there anything I can do? Anything you need?"

First thing they say to chronic fatigue sufferers is, "Stop being so lazy. Just get up, get out, get on with your life. It's all psychological, just a state of mind. Look at strong, healthy me compared to tired, helpless you. Gives you an idea of what a little positive thinking can do."

They wanted that warm smile, that firm handshake from me. They wanted the confidence that wasn't there, and the energy I still didn't have.

Who knows what they wanted? But with each interview I went on, I realized more and more they didn't want me. Not that me, anyway. They wanted some other me — the perfect me.

When they asked me to tell them about my greatest

achievement, I lied. I said it was the year we won the National Championship in rugby. I said it was the impact I made on society, working for Senator Wilson on Capitol Hill. I said it was making the Dean's List, though I really can't remember making the Dean's List, so that must have been a lie, too. And they liked that. They liked the sound of it. They liked the way I looked when I said it. Most of all they liked the way the achievements I disclosed mirrored the responses they gave, while sitting where I sat staring at the apostles of employment across the cherry wood table years before.

Unfortunately, my deception never went far enough, the real me rearing its head at inauspicious moments. I was like the used car salesman in that episode of *The Twilight Zone* who buys a car that forces him to tell the truth:

USED CAR LOT - DAY

SALESMAN
Hi, how are you folks doing today?

COUPLE
We're fine. Thanks.

SALESMAN
The car you're looking at there is the nicest one on the lot. Just came in yesterday. She sure is a beauty, isn't she?

HUSBAND
She sure is.

SALESMAN
You should see the engine. It's practically brand new.

WIFE
Really?

246

SALESMAN
Well, it's almost brand new. Actually, it's not new at all. In fact, I'd be surprised if it makes it off the lot.

COUPLE
What?

SALESMAN
Actually what I meant to say was, wouldn't you like to take it for a spin around the block?

HUSBAND
We sure would.

SALESMAN
Well, I wouldn't. You couldn't get me to ride in that old heap if you paid me.

COUPLE
What'd you just say?

SALESMAN
I said, the sticker price is so low on this baby you probably think I'm crazy.

HUSBAND
You are crazy, Mister. Let's get out of here, honey.

WIFE
Yes, let's.

SALESMAN
No, wait! Just take a look at this car over here. I'm asking four times what paid for it. I mean, I don't deserve half of what I'm asking for it. I mean, I don't know what I mean ...

247

... or something like that. Can't remember exactly how the episode went, but you catch my drift. Just as they (my interviewers, my interrogators, trying to make me talk) weren't buying into my charade, I sure as hell wasn't buying into theirs either. Bunch of stuffed shirts, and faux fat cats. I saw the world going the wrong way — profit, greed, modernity. I just wanted to share a few of my insights because I felt I was right and this job search thing was all wrong. It wasn't going well at all.

I still wasn't fully recovered. I was concerned that if I landed a full-time job, I wouldn't be able to work the hours; maintain a steady course of health and well-being. I was afraid and the fear was written across my face. Fatigue set deep in my eyes, particularly during interviews in which I was forced to meet with several people in one sitting.

Waiting in a cushioned chair, in the meeting room of an office suite in Century City, Beverly Hills, Woodland Hills, downtown Los Angeles — it all seemed the same — each new person that walked into the room carried a clipboard and a slate of questions.

As the minutes, sometimes hours, progressed, I found it harder and harder just to keep my eyes open. Maybe you can feign intellect, feign interest, even feign desire to be the right person for the job, but it's impossible to feign vitality. Maybe you can for a little while, smile and look attentive.

Soon your shoulders slouch as you become more ensconced in your plush, high-back, cushioned chair. Your mind starts to wander. In between breaks you're tossing water on your face.

"Wake up! You're almost through this."

Then it's over and you hope maybe next time things will go a little better. And they do, but it doesn't matter, because the guy/girl whom they interviewed before you knows the boss' son/daughter — an old friend of the family. The company never calls you back to let you know their decision had nothing to do with you or that you weren't qualified or that they didn't like you. What was merely an issue of filial obligation becomes that all-too-familiar feeling of failure and rejection.

Next day, you're back at the U.C.L.A. job board — slack-jawed, slump-stooped, head hung low because of the albatross around your neck. You didn't get that job. Will you ever get a job? You're frantically writing down names, scrawling out numbers so you can go home and send out five more resumes and cover letters.

You see the same job-seekers you saw last week, except that one person whom you always saw on previous visits, who's not there now and you say to yourself:

"Bet that guy got a job. Lucky bastard."

Then you see something, an opportunity, something really sweet; the job that would make you forget all those endless rejections; the one that, when you finish reading the description, you can't help thinking, "Hey, that's me. I'm perfect for this job. This is exactly what I want to do with my life. Exactly the direction I want to take." The cycle starts all over again — cover letters, interviews, press the flesh, dawn that winning smile, and send out thank-you cards. You try so hard.

It gets to a point where you're willing to consider just about anything that pays a buck.

"'Lick tires clean with my tongue for five bucks an hour.' Sure — that sounds great. Always wanted to be a tire-licker."

But, that doesn't pan out either, 'cause your tongue wasn't long enough.

Finally you get the job you're looking for. It may take a month, six months, a year, but it happens. When it rains it pours — three job offers in one week. You take the best offer you can get. It puts you on the map, like that first pin, your starting point for all the places you want to go. Turn down the other two, which feels good — nice to reject someone else for a change — and run with it, which is what I did.

Epilogue

Chapter 30

What did I do, diddle-dee-doo. More than you know, diddle-dee-dee. Stepped back in the world, you see. Crawled, clawed, scraped, and climbed, then let go, like snow flakes falling. So beautiful to announce, "I'm finally here."

I started seeing yet another Chinese herbalist the summer I graduated from college — another recommendation from my roommate's friend/my friend Al; the friend who started dating my high school girlfriend, and later moved with her to Dallas, TX. After all these years, what a strange small world we live in.

Interestingly, Daniel, my herbalist, shared offices with the same herbalist I went to when my illness first began — the herbalist whose alcohol-based herbs made my stomach ache, my body stiff with toxicity, and caused diarrhea like acid rain, to stream from my backside; caused me to lose twenty-five pounds in three months.

Sitting in Daniel's office on my first visit, I said, "You know I've been here before. It was probably about four years ago."

"Oh yeah, who did you see?"

"I can't remember his name."

"Was it Matt?"

"No, I don't think so."

"Joe?"

"No. Well maybe I'm wrong. Maybe I haven't been here." I couldn't quite remember. "But you know, he used one of those metal trays in treating me."

253

"What metal tray?"

"The one right there on your desk. He would try to pull apart my fingers and if they came apart easily something was wrong with me, and if they didn't, I was okay."

"That's just a piece of aluminum."

"Yeah, but I know he *used* it."

Panic started to settle in. What the hell was I doing here? I went this route once before and paid dearly for it — the herbs were one of the primary reasons I was forced to withdraw from Berkeley my senior year. They made my fatigue worse, my mission impossible:

"Try walking a little farther every day," my first herbalist told me. "If you think you can walk to the end of the block, cut that in half, then cut that distance in half again and walk that far. Do that every day and eventually you will get better."

Worse advice I ever received, because it became the basis of my five-year neurosis; walks by which I measured my health in feet, the length of the street, the street signs on long city blocks; signposts to remind me each day how well or how poorly I was doing; signposts to quantify a quality of life that could not be measured.

Yet, here I sat in a similar room, as Daniel the Chinese herbalist, stretched my belief system like a side-long Gumby and Pokie. He used his fingers to poke at my face, chest, back, legs, and feet, checking my acupressure points, then scribbling down the findings of his examination. Tap, tap. Poke, poke, poke. Scribble, scribble.

As he examined me, Daniel ushered various herbs on and off the aluminum tray that initially sparked my fear. He checked and rechecked each herb against the weaknesses found in my acupressure points to determine their value in combating my malaise. Tap, tap, poke. Tap, poke. Scribble, scribble, scribble.

"Are the herbs you use in treating patients alcohol-based liquid herbs, because that's what made me sick the last time. The alcohol really affected my ..."

"No, we don't use those anymore [tap, poke], because some people did have a problem taking them [tap, poke, poke]. Now we grind them up into a powder and you

254

swallow small spoonfuls of the herb formula with water [scribble, scribble, tap, tap, poke]."

That's it, we're all done. I'm going to go mix up this herb formula, then I'll meet you out front. All right?"

"Okay."

That was it. I embarked on my third foray into Chinese herbs, but was I nuts? Maybe. Things were going okay. I was finishing up school, starting to become a bit more active.

Feeling better still wasn't good enough. I wanted to be healthy, play sports, and be able to punish my body; drink wine 'til I was so woozy I puked, then be able to bounce back two days later. Not that I ever would, but you catch my meaning. While I was glad to be feeling better, I wanted to be cured.

The herbs offered no fast and easy solution. Up and down; up, up and down, down. I was on the phone to Daniel at least twice a week. I would be feeling shitty and wiped out, so I'd give him a call.

"Double up," he'd say.

"What do you mean, double up?"

"Take two spoonfuls of herbs every four hours instead of one."

"But I feel like shit. That's just going to make me feel worse."

"Maybe, but I don't think so. This could just be a cleansing period. Try it for a couple days. If it doesn't work, come in and see me."

I hung up the phone feeling bitter, a twist of sarcasm on my face. Once again I was on the downside of a supposed "cleansing period" and knew I probably wouldn't feel any better in couple days and that I might just feel worse. Yet, I promised to give this a try. Many times in the past, I quit treatments after a couple days out of uncertainty and fear, then wondered if I'd stayed on the regimen, if maybe I would have felt better. This time I held the course and doubled up.

Sure enough, after two days I felt better. I didn't feel great or anything, I just didn't feel the tremendous fatigue and exhaustion I experienced initially.

This process went on for several months. Each new batch of herbs — grubby brown granules spooned from a plastic zip-lock bag — whacked me in some different way. Some herb combinations made my eyes water, others my throat dry. At times my stomach churned with nausea. I felt like a tennis ball being volleyed back and forth in a rally that might never end.

Fortunately, the adverse affects of the herbs were rarely severe and generally manageable, so I stuck with it and continued to get better. I was unsure as to whether it was my body healing naturally, or the herbs helping the process, but it didn't matter. Taking the herbs as my tonic toward better health, enabled me to stop worrying about trying other treatments new fangled and far. When I felt shitty, I took the herbs. When I felt good, I took them anyway. At least they weren't making me worse; at best they were making me better.

After six months of searching, I wasn't able to land a job, and wasn't sure if I could maintain a job once landed. I took plane flights to San Francisco to interview for jobs I wasn't sure I wanted, jobs I wouldn't get. I started temping. Figured maybe I could work part-time, earn some money, test the water on my day-to-day health and still have time to write — the perfect plan.

Ahh, the joy of temping. Underpaid for a job in which you are overskilled and yet decidedly less competent than the person you are replacing, because you don't know where anything is. You don't know how any of the basic processes are handled. And most of the time, the person you are reporting to isn't happy about having to adjust their schedule to accommodate a temp.

Still, I managed to stumble into what I deemed the perfect job — nine-to-five, with an hour for lunch — processing orders and servicing the basic billing requirements of a small publishing group, while the woman I replaced recovered from surgery.

I even had my own office, overlooking a construction site and the unofficial title of Traffic Manager. Stuck a paper plaque on my door with my name on it; looked and sounded official.

I befriended many of the interesting characters who worked in the office. Nancy, the friendly overweight mail room clerk, who handled all mail sorting and office supply purchasing. Nancy, who never worked even a minute longer than she was required, who always took a full one-hour lunch break and was writing a murder mystery in her free time.

Michael, the office manager, who, from his de facto office — de facto in that no one else was using it so by association, or lack thereof, it became his — was always managing something, though I never figured out what. He liked to comment on the clothes I wore.

"Nice shirt, very nice. I love the jacket. How much did you pay for it?"

"I can't remember, I've had it for a while."

"Oh, its nice all right — very sporty."

"Thanks."

Chris, the striving young actor cum intern, who, after a full two years in Los Angeles, a degree in theater and film from U.C.L.A., two commercials, and a series of bit roles in low-budget plays, would be returning home to Tennessee to take the MCATs, a few pre-med courses and apply to medical school to become a family practitioner. He liked to play it cool — the mellow, down-to-earth type.

"What's up, Chris?"

"Not much."

"Cool."

And Iris, the neurotic, albeit extremely kind VP of marketing who'd always had three too many cups of coffee and a pack of cigarettes on her coffee break — very sharp, very intense. She offered me a job as sales assistant once my temporary position ended, which I regretfully declined. I mean, sure — I was a temp, but I certainly wasn't going to work as someone's secretary.

Not that I have a problem with secretaries, mind you, or that I feel secretarial work is beneath me, but I certainly wasn't going to keep someone else's files. Nor would I type their letters, and basically make them look good on my time in a job I could probably do better myself. I'm no egomaniac either, but secretarial work just wasn't my bag.

Things went well with my temporary three-month position. I earned some money. My competence gave me the confidence that I could hold a full-time position. Nothing too strenuous, no fourteen-hour days, but a reasonable work schedule was in reach.

If I was going to work full-time and be forced to sacrifice my writing time on the side, I decided I might as well get a job where I stood a chance of moving up. I applied for and landed a job at a medium-sized public relations agency as Account Coordinator — a.k.a. low dog on a totem pole so tall it stretched the sky.

It was like a dream come true. Really, I mean it. Skip, skip, skipping along, like a six-year-old that hooked a big fat fish on a skinny fiberglass rod: "I got one! I got one!"

In fact, I received three job offers in the same week. One from the public relations firm; one from the small publishing company I was working for as a temp; and one from a company that specialized in producing video news releases for government and corporate clients.

Forced to make a decision, I chose the mid-sized public relations firm. If I was going to go corporate, thought I might as well go with a known company. Besides, the pay was a little better — not much better, but a little. Criminal how much they started out paying me. Could people actually live on that? Guess so. I did.

My new job status planted me firmly in corporate America — a *salaree* man. Suit. Tie. White-collared shirt starched stiff. Clocking in, clocking out, day in day out. Health care and dental benefits. A 401K plan, cause you gotta plan for retirement — all those years you won't work; all those days you're gonna sit out on your balcony whittling wood, or planting vegetables, or seeding the lawn, or painting with watercolors. All those things retirees do. Maybe take a cruise or two — or three or four. Or, better yet, play cards down at the local yacht club, before cruising out on your sixty-five foot schooner — the American Dream. A raucous bunch of silver hairs getting in a few last kicks before they kick — off. You gotta plan for retirement.

Funny thing was, I didn't know the first thing about public relations. Knew even less about high-tech public relations (i.e. public relations for the computer industry). Still, I picked up a couple computer trade publications, studied them, and charged into my interview with a gung-ho smile and about as much BS as I could muster.

Chris, the general manager of the L.A. office, was larger than I imagined after talking to him on the phone — six-feet-four, and close to three hundred pounds. Leaning back in an oversized leather chair, he asked me the usual:

"So, tell me about yourself."

To which I generally gave a recap of my resume, stressing the highlights as they pertained to the job. Except now I had been working a couple months, my spiel was a bit more finely tuned. My energy remained strong, not fading in and out like a Walkman using up its final volts from a set of overused, double-A batteries. I could point to real situations as examples of my competence in the workplace.

"Well, it sounds like you're a pretty good writer. Do you know how to write a press release?"

"Sure, no problem," I replied.

"Are you a good speller?"

"Yeah, I'd say I'm pretty good at that."

"Great, because there's a writing test I'd like to give you before you leave."

"Okay." I'm thinking, "Writing test?" I'm feeling a bit nervous, because while I'm a decent speller, I don't have a clue as to what a press release is, or what it should look like.

A three-page test lay down on a desk in a quiet room, just like finals back in college or high school. The only thing I could think to cull from is Journalism 101 — who, what, when, where, why and how answered in the first paragraph, then take it from there.

My task, should I be capable of performing it: write a press release announcing the invention of scissors. An absurd topic, but one I could have fun with, so I did. Threw in a few quotes describing the juxtaposition of two metal slicing surfaces held together by an iron pin, that, when merged, was capable of cutting paper, string and fabric of varying compositions.

I turned it in, shook Chris's hand, and walked out, feeling pretty good about my prospects. He called me at work two days later at the small publishing house, where my time was just about up, to offer me the job. My first real job, starting on a Monday. Just like the way *they* always told me it would be, except it was six years and what seemed like a lifetime later. I was entering in through the back door, on the ground floor, after a long tired journey that was just beginning and would not stop here.

Healthier. Older. Wiser. One year later, I stood watering the yard from the balcony of my mom's house in Los Feliz; my roommate Dave inhaling his cancer through the filtered end of a cigarette butt; the evening sky awash with clouds, purple, grey and black at dusk after a long, hot summer day in Los Angeles.

My herbalist declared me cured, though I still from time to time felt the drag of a hard day at work — the muscle soreness after an overdone workout, which people told me was normal. However, I couldn't help wonder if my normal was like their normal, or if it was something completely different. I couldn't help wonder if they would ever understand that nothing was normal beyond the outward shell of appearance and comparison. That life turns like a snake, in and out of holes, slithering along, sometimes slower than fast, most times faster than slow. The beauty and the pain all wrapped up in the turning. The same force that leaves you cold and lifeless, ensures your spirit lives, forever burning.

CONSAFOS PRESS
Publishers of Art Books, and Alternative Non-Fiction

For information about other books available from Consafos, and how to order them, write to the address provided below, or visit us on the Web at: www.consafos.com.

To order additional copies of *Dazed and Fatigued in the Toxic 21st Century,* you can use this order form page:

❖ Telephone credit card orders call toll free 1-800-655-4897

❖ Postal Orders send check or money order to:

Consafos Press
P.O. Box 931568
Los Angeles, CA 90093

Name:_____

Address:_____

City:_____ State:_____ Zip:_____

Telephone: (_____) _____

E-Mail : _____

Please add $3.00 shipping and handling, plus tax when applicable (8.25% for books shipped to California addresses).